LAUBACH WAY TO
Reading 3

A time-tested method that has taught millions of adults to read

WORKBOOK

JEANETTE D. MACERO

New Readers Press
ProLiteracy's publishing division

Laubach Way to Reading 3 Workbook
ISBN 978-1-56420-937-5

Copyright © 2011, 1991, 1983 New Readers Press
New Readers Press
ProLiteracy's Publishing Division
104 Marcellus Street, Syracuse, New York 13204
www.newreaderspress.com

Printed in the United States of America
9 8 7 6 5

Proceeds from the sale of New Readers Press materials support professional development, training, and technical assistance programs of ProLiteracy that benefit local literacy programs in the U.S. and around the globe.

Developmental Editor: Terrie Lipke
Creative Director: Andrea Woodbury
Production Specialist: Maryellen Casey
Art and Design Supervisor: James P. Wallace
Illustrations: Drew Rose, represented by Wilkinson Studios, Inc.
Cover Design: Carolyn Wallace

Table of Contents

Table of Contents

This workbook is designed to give students additional practice in listening to, speaking, reading, and writing the patterns of English presented in *Laubach Way to Reading 3*. The vocabulary is correlated to each lesson level in book 3, although some new words are introduced.

The workbook gives practice in 15 skill areas, all of which are important in mastering English. (See the scope and sequence chart on page 6.) There are exercises on the singular and plural forms of nouns and on the use of articles and prepositions. There are many opportunities for the student to learn verb forms and tenses and to make and answer questions in the affirmative and negative. Students practice writing sentences both by writing original sentences and by combining two sentences into one. Students fill out forms to get practice in answering typical questions found on applications for credit cards, marriage licenses, and parking permits.

A major type of exercise in the workbook is the cloze exercise, here titled Story with Missing Words. These exercises are passages from book 3 stories in which every nth word (from 5th to 9th) is left out, except for names or numbers that would be impossible to figure out from context. Any appropriate word—that is, any word that is both grammatically correct and logical—is acceptable as an answer. In this type of exercise, the student is required to integrate *all* of his language skills. Cloze exercises are thus significantly different from exercises that focus on only one skill at a time.

Listening exercises are included to sharpen the students' ability to hear the difference between singular and plural forms, full and contracted forms of verbs, and verb endings. These forms are often difficult for students to differentiate.

An answer key is provided at the back of the book. Students should be discouraged from looking at the answers while they are doing the exercises. At times you may allow students to check their own work, but *you* should check their work as much as possible so that you can help them understand and correct their errors. Also, your judgment is needed in cases where more than one answer is possible. Be sure to praise students for their correct answers. If a student gives correct answers that are not shown in the key, praise him for showing knowledge of the language beyond that expected or already taught.

How to Use the Exercises

The exercises for each lesson are arranged in increasing order of difficulty. Some exercise pages have a note at the bottom that gives specific instructions to the teacher. In general, however, the following steps are useful for the majority of exercises.

1. Teach any new words listed at the top of the page. Students should be able to sound out most of the new words; phonetic respellings are provided where necessary. If a word is marked with an asterisk, however, tell the students what the word is. The asterisk indicates a sight word containing a sound or spelling not yet taught.
2. Read the directions orally with the students. Never assign an exercise without being sure that the students know what is required in it.
3. Go over the two examples that are given for each exercise.

The answer is always supplied for the first example and sometimes for the second. If the second example is blank, ask students to do it on their own. If the second example is filled in, have them do the first exercise item. Then check their work. Praise them if they have the correct answer. If a student's answer is incorrect, explain the error. Have the student write the correct answer and read the item aloud. If a student still cannot do the exercise, go over the examples again and do one or two exercise items with him.

4. Have students follow the directions carefully and keep the sentences in the tenses given.

Tips on Specific Types of Exercises

Most exercises for a particular lesson can be assigned as homework, along with the homework for that lesson in book 3.

Cloze exercises. In the Story with Missing Words exercises, students are to fill in *one* word in each blank. Encourage them to search for context clues that will help them figure out the word to write. Have students both look back and read ahead to find clues. Teach them how to figure out what words are appropriate for any given blank. In the cloze exercise "My Class" in Lesson 1, there is this sentence: *Carla Lopez works at a _____ shop.* By reading ahead in the paragraph, students find that Carla works in a music shop. They must use the word *music* since some other word, although it might be grammatically correct, would not fit logically into the paragraph.

If a cloze exercise is done in class, there is no time limit for finishing it. After students have completed a story, go over it and explain any errors.

If a cloze exercise is done as homework, students may check their answers against the corresponding passage in book 3. You should also look over students' completed passages. For one thing, you can judge whether their answers are acceptable when they have not used the exact word given in the skill book. (In Lesson 10, for example, there is this sentence: *After fourteen years, I _____ my repair shop.* Although the skill book uses the word *started*, the word *opened* would also be acceptable.) Also, you will want to see what kinds of errors students are making, such as errors with verb forms, prepositions, or articles. Then you can consult the scope and sequence chart to find exercises in students' specific problem areas.

Word order. Stress the importance of word order in English, but do not go into detail about possible variations of word order. It is best in declarative sentences to stress this order: subject, verb, object(s), place, and time.

Verb tenses. Point out the words (for example, *now, yesterday*) that indicate the tense to be used. Also, point out the necessary sequence of tenses in sentences. In the sentence *When I was nineteen, I (get) a job with a hockey team*, the use of *was* in the first clause requires the use of *got* in the main clause.

Writing sentences. Go over the original sentences the students write. Check for errors, and explain in simple terms anything that is wrong with the sentences. Praise students for whatever they can write correctly. If students cannot write sentences on their own, do some sample sentences orally. Have students write these sentences. Then reassign the exercises for homework, asking students to write different sentences.

Listening exercises. Unlike other exercises, these must be done in class. In most of these exercises, students see a pair of sentences that are the same except for the items being contrasted, for example: *He makes $16 a week* and *He makes $60 a week*. Students are to mark the sentence that you say. You may read either of the sentences in each pair.

Do the examples with students, repeating them if necessary. Read the sentences in a natural manner at a regular pace. Do not emphasize the items being contrasted or enunciate the words with extra care. Pick one sentence from the first pair, and read it twice. Then go on to the next pair.

If students have difficulty with a listening exercise, do it again. Read different sentences from the pairs the second time.

How to Vary the Exercises

While most of the exercises were designed primarily to be used as homework, they may also be used to advantage in class or while tutoring.

1. Some of the exercises may be done orally with books closed. Help students with their pronunciation and intonation at this time.
2. Have students do the exercises as homework. Then, at the next class session, have them read the answers to you. Listen for pronunciation and intonation errors. Have students imitate your pronunciation of words, phrases, and sentences that cause them difficulty. In a class situation, students can work in pairs with one student asking the questions (for example) and the other answering them.
3. Some exercises can be used for dictation, for example, the listening exercises, the completed Stories with Missing Words, and any verb form exercises. First, read the entire sentence at a normal pace; do not enunciate in an exaggerated manner. Next, dictate the sentence in meaningful segments, reading each segment twice.

When dictation is still difficult for students, the sentence *After work, / I will pick up / my friend / David Miller* can be read in the segments marked by the slashes. As students become more proficient with dictation exercises, the segments can be longer and can be read once instead of twice, for example: *After work, / I will pick up / my friend David Miller* or *After work, I will pick up / my friend David Miller*.

Give students time to look over what they have written. Read the sentence again at a normal pace so students can check any parts they have doubts about.

Finally, have students correct their sentences according to the model in the workbook. If they make their corrections in a different color, you can easily see what mistakes they are making. It is important for you to look over the dictation. The errors will give you invaluable insight into students' learning processes and show you where students need more practice.

Scope and Sequence
Skill Areas in Workbook 3 Lessons by Practice Numbers

Skill areas Lesson	1	2	3	4	5	6	7	8	9	10	11	12	13	14	15	16	17	18	19	20	21	22	23	24
1. Nouns	3	1, 4						3																
2. Pronouns								4							1	1								
3. Verbs	1		3, 4		2, 3			2	1, 3			1			2		4		3, 4, 5, 6			3, 4		
4. Prepositions	2					2						2		1			2, 3	1						4
5. Articles			1			1					1													
6. Make questions	4			3	1				4				3	2						4				
7. Answer questions		5					1			2									4, 6			4		
8. Make negative sentences				2																	1		1	
9. Word order in sentences		2		1	3				2				2	3							2	1		
10. Make new words								5											1, 2	1				1
11. Combine sentences		3				4	2			1	2							2	7	2				
12. Write sentences								5			3		1		3	3	5			3	3	2	2	2, 3
13. Story with missing words	5				4		3	6		3		3		5		4		3		5		5	3	
14. Read and fill in forms			2					1		4	5		4						6				
15. Listen							4		5	4		4	4		5		4							

| practice (prac tis) | example (eg zam pul) | preposition (prep u zish un) |
| verb | goes (gōz) | |

PRACTICE 1: Verbs

Write the missing verb.

Examples: Carla _____**has**_____ fun.
have, has

Ted _____ with his mother.
live, lives

1. My friend _____ at a factory.
work, works

2. She _____ to class with us.
go, goes

3. Carla Lopez _____ at a music shop.
work, works

4. I _____ fun.
has, have

5. We _____ to music.
listen, listens

PRACTICE 2: Prepositions

Write the preposition *at*, *on*, or *in*.

Examples: Carla works _____**at**_____ a music shop.

She lives _____ the city.

1. I work _____ a market.

2. We can get a quick snack _____ Fran's.

3. He works _____ York Street.

4. We go to class _____ my car.

5. David lives _____ First Street.

6. He works _____ 615 York Street.

7. We study hard _____ class.

8. We write _____ the paper.

PRACTICE 3: Singular and Plural Forms of Nouns

Write the singular or the plural form of the missing noun.

Examples: I'll have a _____*glass*_____ of milk.
glass

I'll have two _____ of milk.
glass

1. The _____ is Jason's.
car

2. My _____ are in class with me.
friend

3. The _____ is on York Street.
shop

4. The _____ are in the kitchen.
box

5. I listen to _____.
music

6. She writes a _____ to Carla.
letter

7. The _____ are in the kitchen.
dish

8. The _____ are egg salad.
sandwich

9. She has two _____.
bill

10. The _____ are Kitty's.
dress

make (māk)	question (ques chun)	use (ūz)

PRACTICE 4: Make Questions with *who*

Make a question from the sentence. Use *who*.

Examples: Fran works at a pet shop.

Who __**works at a pet shop**_____?

David lives at 917 First Street.

Who _____?

1. Jason has a car.

   Who _____?

2. Carla works at a music shop.

   Who _____?

3. Ms. Smith is a nurse.

   Who _____?

4. Carla, David, and I will go for a snack.

   Who _____?

5. David lives at 917 First Street.

   Who _____?

6. David and I go to Fran's Snack Shop.

   Who _____?

7. I work hard.

   Who _____?

8. Jason and David go to class after work.

   Who _____?

PRACTICE 5: Story with Missing Words

Write the missing words.

My Class

   I am Jason Hunt. I work at a market on River _____.

I go to class after work. I _____ some paper. The paper is

for my _____.

   After work, I will pick up my _____ David Miller.

He works at a factory _____ York Street. I will pick

up David _____ the factory. We will go to class

_____ my car.

   Carla Lopez works at a _____ shop on York Street.

We will pick _____ Carla at the music shop. She will

_____ to class with us.

   We will study _____ in class. We will study the lesson.

_____ will write on the paper. We will write sentences.

PRACTICE 1: Singular and Plural Forms of Nouns

1. Write the noun.

2. Write the noun in a sentence.

Examples:

1. <u>dollars</u>
2. <u>I have two dollars.</u>

1. <u>table</u>
2. <u>I work at the table.</u>

1. _____
2. _____

1. _____
2. _____

1. _____
2. _____

1. _____
2. _____

1. _____
2. _____

1. _____
2. _____

right (rīt)   order (or der)

PRACTICE 2: Word Order in Sentences

Put the words in the right order to make a sentence.

Examples: I shop work a music in.

I ___work in a music shop._____

Rosa me with is kitchen in the.

Rosa _____

1. a table the on radio is.

   A _____

2. Rosa baby my is.

   Rosa _____

3. I at months six have for worked music shop the.

   I _____

4. it six past is half.

   It _____

5. not April bad a month was.

   April _____

6. loves baby my her.

   My _____

combine (com bīn)

PRACTICE 3: Combine Sentences

Make one sentence from two. Use *that*.

Examples: I am happy. I am in this class.

<u>I am happy that I am in this class.</u>

I am happy. Carla has a babysitter for Rosa.

_____

1. David is happy. Carla is his friend.

_____

2. Carla is happy. David helps her with Rosa.

_____

3. Carla is happy. Mrs. King loves Rosa.

_____

4. Carla is happy. David is coming to dinner.

_____

5. I am happy. Rosa is singing.

_____

6. I am happy. I am in this class.

_____

7. David is happy. He can help Carla in class.

_____

8. I am happy. You are my friend.

_____

PRACTICE 4: Write the Missing Words

Write *a glass, a cup, a pat, a box,* or *a jar.*

Examples: _____a glass_____ of milk   _____ of water

1. _____ of butter   5. _____ of milk

2. _____ of coffee   6. _____ of water

3. _____ of jelly   7. _____ of matches

4. _____ of instant potatoes

PRACTICE 5: Answer Questions

Write the answers to the questions.
You are in Fran's Snack Shop. You want a snack.

Examples: What will you have?

   I'll have a ham sandwich. _____

What will you have?

_____

1. What will you have?

_____

2. What will you have?

_____

3. What will you have?

_____

4. What will you have to drink?

_____

5. What will you have to drink?

_____

Note: Be sure the student orders something different in each answer.

PRACTICE 1: *a, an, the*

Write *a, an,* or *the.*

Examples: ___The___ Masons are writing checks.

Kay writes _____ check for _____ rent.

_____ Masons live in _____ apartment in _____ city. They are paying their bills today. Ray is looking at _____ bills. Kay is writing _____ checks. _____ Masons have to pay _____ lot of bills in May. They have to pay _____ telephone bill for April. They have to pay _____ water bill for three months. They have to pay Kay's doctor bill. It was for _____ office visit.

PRACTICE 2: Write a Check

Today is April 2. You are paying your bills. You have a bill from the babysitter. The bill is for $125.00. The babysitter's name is Molly King. Write the check to pay your bill. Write your name on the check.

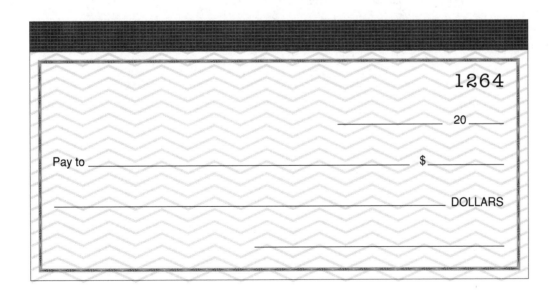

tense (tens)   *now

PRACTICE 3: Verb Tenses

Write *am*, *is*, *are*, *was*, or *were*.

Examples: I _____ *am* _____ looking at the paper now.

She _____ in class yesterday.

1. I _____ Carla Lopez.

2. It _____ half past six now.

3. David and I _____ friends now.

4. Rosa is a baby. She _____ happy when she _____ with Mrs. King.

5. I _____ in class yesterday.

6. David and Ted _____ at Fran's Snack Shop yesterday.

7. Yesterday _____ payday for Kay and Ray Mason.

8. Their next payday _____ May 15.

9. The Masons _____ paying their bills today.

10. Kay _____ writing a check for the rent now.

PRACTICE 4: Verb Tenses

Use the right form of the verb in the sentence.

Examples: I (work) _____**work**_____ at a factory every day.

I (work) _____**worked**_____ at the factory yesterday.

I (work) __**have worked**__ at the factory for six months.

1. I (live) _____ on Garden Street.

   I (live) _____ on York Street last April.

   I (live) _____ on Garden Street for six months.

2. The Masons (put) _____ $750 in the bank every payday.

   The Masons (put) _____ $750 in the bank last payday.

   The Masons (put) _____ $750 in the bank every payday for six months.

3. Jason (run) _____ in the park every day.

   Jason (run) _____ in the park yesterday.

   Jason (run) _____ in the park every day for two months.

4. Mrs. King (help) _____ Carla with Rosa every day.

   Mrs. King (help) _____ Carla with Rosa yesterday.

   Mrs. King (help) _____ Carla with Rosa for ten months.

PRACTICE 1: Word Order in Sentences

Add the words to the sentence.

Examples: (with me)   Rosa is in the kitchen.

Rosa   **is with me in the kitchen.** _____

(gray)   They got two quarts of paint.

They _____

1. (in April)   I started work.

   I _____

2. (with me)   My baby cannot go to work.

   My baby _____

3. (a lot of)   The Masons have to pay bills in May.

   The Masons _____

4. (doctor)   They have to pay Kay's bill.

   They _____

5. (with us)   Carla and David can come and play cards.

   Carla and David _____

6. (then)   And we will not have many bills.

   And we _____

7. (next)   We can go away after the payday.

   We _____

8. (in May)   Let's go away the last three days.

   Let's _____

9. (for the rent)   Kay writes a check.

   Kay _____

10. (your name)   Write on the check.

    Write _____

negative (neg u tiv)

PRACTICE 2: Make Negative Sentences

Add *not* to the sentence.

Examples: I have painted a kitchen.

**I have not painted a kitchen.**

The landlady can fix the stairs.

**The landlady cannot fix the stairs.**

1. I have painted chairs.

_____

2. Let's paint the kitchen red.

_____

3. Jason will fix the stairs.

_____

4. Let's paint the stairs first.

_____

5. Gail has had lunch.

_____

6. You have painted the table and chairs.

_____

7. They will paint the kitchen red.

_____

8. Rosa can go to work with Carla.

_____

9. Let's play cards today.

_____

10. We can live on two hundred dollars.

_____

PRACTICE 3: Make Questions

Make a question from the sentence.

Examples: You will paint the kitchen.

   _Will you paint the kitchen______?

   You have painted the kitchen.

   _____?

1. We will paint the kitchen.

   _____?

2. Gail has had paint in her hair.

   _____?

3. You can fix the stairs first.

   _____?

4. We shall paint the kitchen red.

   _____?

5. Jason will fix the stairs first.

   _____?

6. She has painted the chairs.

   _____?

7. Jason and Gail can paint the kitchen pink.

   _____?

8. You will pay for the paint.

   _____?

9. We shall paint the stairs first.

   _____?

PRACTICE 1: Make Questions with Question Words

Make a question from the sentence. Use a question mark.

Examples: Jason and Gail got married in Gail's church.

Where   **_did Jason and Gail get married?_** _____

Jason gave Gail some cake.

What _____

1. Jason's mother baked the wedding cake.

Who _____

2. The party was in a building next to the church.

Where _____

3. They had the party after the wedding.

When _____

4. The wedding cake was on a pretty glass plate.

Where _____

5. Gail and Jason are still in the church.

Where _____

6. Gail's uncle will take a picture of the wedding cake.

What _____

7. Gail is writing a thank you letter to Carla.

Who _____

8. Gail and Jason got many wedding gifts.

What _____

Note: After this exercise, students will be expected to use question marks
where they are necessary without being told to do so.

PRACTICE 2: Verb Forms

Write a sentence. Tell the person what to do.

Examples: Tell Don to get a gallon of paint.

Don, get a gallon of paint.

Tell Jane not to paint the chair.

Jane, don't paint the chair.

1. Tell Jane to have a cup of coffee.

_____

2. Tell Jane to listen to music on the radio.

_____

3. Tell Kay to pay the bills.

_____

4. Tell Jason to paint the kitchen first.

_____

5. Tell Kitty not to put milk in the pan.

_____

6. Tell Tom not to go away now.

_____

7. Tell Jimmy not to yell at us.

_____

8. Tell Gail not to paint the stairs first.

_____

22   Lesson 5

PRACTICE 3: Verb Forms

Answer the question with a sentence.
Use *let's* or *let's not* in your answer.

Examples: Shall we go away in May?

Yes, __**let's go away in May.**__

Shall you and I paint the chairs red?

No, __**let's not paint the chairs red.**__

1. Shall we listen to music on the radio?

Yes, _____

2. Shall you and I take the children to the wedding?

No, _____

3. Shall we stop at the bank after work today?

No, _____

4. Shall you and I telephone Jane?

Yes, _____

5. Shall we have some cake?

Yes, _____

6. Shall you and I take Liz to the party with us?

Yes, _____

7. Shall we paint the kitchen gray?

No, _____

8. Shall we get two gallons of paint?

Yes, _____

PRACTICE 4: Story with Missing Words

Write the missing words.

The Wedding

Jason and Gail got married in Gail's church. Jason's family and friends came to the wedding. Gail's family and friends came. After the _____, there was a party. The party was _____ a building next to the church.

At _____ party, there was a big wedding cake. _____ was on a pretty glass plate. There _____ little sandwiches, coffee, and other drinks. There _____ paper plates and cups.

"Take a plate _____ help yourself to sandwiches," said Gail's sister Jane. "_____ help yourself to drinks."

"May I have _____ cake?" asked Jason's little brother Sam.

"No, _____ yet," said Jane. "Jason and Gail have _____ cut the cake first."

"Where are they?" _____ Sam.

"They are still in the church," Jane _____. "Gail's uncle is still taking pictures of _____. He will take a picture of the _____ cake when they cut it."

"Who baked _____ wedding cake?" asked Carla.

Jane said, "Jason's mother baked it. She bakes many wedding cakes."

PRACTICE 1: *a, an, the*

Write *a*, *an*, or *the*.

Examples: **The** Masons are writing checks.

Kay writes _____ check for _____ rent.

1. Carla and David came to _____ Masons' apartment.

2. Kay put four chairs at _____ card table.

3. She works in _____ office in _____ big building.

4. I'll have _____ cup of coffee.

5. They played in _____ water.

6. Gail and Jason were having _____ snack.

7. There was _____ quart of milk on _____ table.

8. You are _____ dear friend.

9. Ted had _____ egg salad sandwich.

10. He will take _____ picture of _____ wedding cake.

11. Will you have _____ apple?

12. Who cut _____ cake?

PRACTICE 2: Prepositions *to* and *for*

Write *to* or *for*.

Examples: David came _____**to**_____ Carla's apartment.

He came _____ dinner.

1. I will pay you _____ it.

2. Gail's family and friends came _____ the wedding.

3. Thank you _____ the picture frame.

4. Gail said _____ the others, "Come and help yourself _____ some cake."

5. Kay writes a check _____ the rent.

6. Is Carla listening _____ the radio?

7. Yesterday was payday _____ Kay and Ray Mason.

8. After work, I go _____ class.

9. I have lived in this apartment _____ ten months.

10. I have some paper. The paper is _____ my class.

11. They went away _____ the last three days in May.

12. Kay and Ray went _____ Snake River.

PRACTICE 3: Word Order in Sentences

Add the words to the sentence.

Examples: (with me)   Rosa is in the kitchen.

Rosa __is with me in the kitchen.__

(gray)   They got two quarts of paint.

They _____

1. (never)   I have painted a kitchen.

I _____

2. (black)   Shall we get some paint?

Shall _____

3. (first)   Let's paint the kitchen.

Let's _____

4. (them)   Their landlady paid for the pink paint.

Their landlady _____

5. (one gallon of)   They got gray paint.

They _____

6. (some)   There were sandwiches and a quart of milk on the table.

There _____

7. (in Gail's church)   Jason and Gail got married.

Jason _____

8. (glass)   It was on a pretty plate.

It _____

9. (still)   I have not kissed my little girl.

I _____

10. (many)   She bakes wedding cakes.

She _____

PRACTICE 4: Combine Sentences

Make one sentence from two.

Examples: Carla has an apartment. It is pretty.

Carla **has a pretty apartment.**

Rosa is sitting at the table. Rosa is singing.

Rosa **is sitting at the table and singing.**

1. Carla works at a shop. It is a music shop.

   Carla _____

2. We can have a snack. We can listen to music.

   We _____

3. David has a car. It is black.

   David _____

4. I'll have a ham sandwich. I'll have a glass of milk.

   I'll _____

5. I am listening to music. The music is on the radio.

   I _____

6. You can paint the stairs. You can paint the kitchen.

   You _____

7. She paid for the pink paint. She paid for the gray paint.

   She _____

8. The wedding cake was on a pretty plate. The plate was glass.

   The _____

9. They had coffee. They watched TV.

   They _____

10. They had ham. They had potatoes.

   They _____

PRACTICE 1: Answer the Questions

Write a short answer to the questions.

Examples: Was Mrs. Green sleeping?   No, ___*she wasn't.*_____

                Did you bake this cake?   Yes, _____

1. Is dinner ready?   Yes, _____

2. Did Lee's mother take away his car?   No, _____

3. Were you drinking beer?   No, _____

4. Do I see a cut on your face?   Yes, _____

5. Did you hit the tree?   Yes, _____

6. Did Jason and Gail get married in Gail's apartment?   No, _____

7. Was Mrs. Green sitting in the kitchen?   No, _____

8. Was Lee's mother angry?   Yes, _____

9. Is Gail writing thank you letters?   Yes, _____

10. Were Jason and Gail sitting in the kitchen and having a snack?

    Yes, _____

11. Was Carla getting dinner for ten people yesterday?   No, _____

12. Do Carla and David play cards?   Yes, _____

PRACTICE 2: Combine Sentences

Make one sentence from two. Use *and, when,* or *but.*

Examples: Mrs. Green was in bed. She wasn't sleeping.

Mrs. Green was in bed, but she wasn't sleeping.

Lee came in. His mother got up.

When Lee came in, his mother got up.

1. I cannot sleep. You come in late.

   _____

2. I wasn't going fast. I wasn't drinking beer.

   _____

3. My car still runs. The tree that I hit looks bad.

   _____

4. I am in bed. I'm not sleeping.

   _____

5. Come in. Have a snack with us.

   _____

6. The friends played cards. The friends listened to music on the radio.

   _____

7. David came into the apartment. He kissed Carla.

   _____

8. They had coffee. They watched TV.

   _____

9. They came back from Snake River. Ray said, "We had fun."

   _____

10. They ate some cake. They did not drink coffee.

   _____

PRACTICE 3: Story with Missing Words

Write the missing words.

Lee's Lesson

Mrs. Green was in bed, but she wasn't sleeping. "Where is Lee," she was thinking. "_____ half past three."

Lee was 16. _____ had a job after class. He _____ his first car.

Mrs. Green heard _____ car. When Lee came in, she _____ up. "Where were you?" she yelled. _____ half past three. Were you drinking _____?"

"No, Mother," said Lee. "I wasn't _____ beer. I was just playing cards _____ my friends."

Mrs. Green said, "I _____ sleep when you come in late. _____ need to be in bed. You _____ your sleep."

"OK," said Lee. "Let's _____ to bed."

"What is that?" his _____ asked. "Do I see a cut _____ your face? Yes, I do see _____ cut."

"It's just a little cut," _____ said. "I went to sleep at _____ wheel. I didn't see the tree. _____ car hit the tree. My face _____ the wheel. But I wasn't going fast. And I wasn't drinking beer!"

PRACTICE 4: Listen

Circle the letter of the sentence that the teacher says.

Examples: a. I fixed Mrs. Green's radio.

                 b. I fixed Mrs. Green's radios.

                 a. Write the answer.

                 b. Write the answers.

1. a. I'll have the hamburger.

     b. I'll have the hamburgers.

2. a. Give me the sandwich.

     b. Give me the sandwiches.

3. a. The bill is on the table.

     b. The bills are on the table.

4. a. They have to pay Kay's doctor bill.

     b. They have to pay Kay's doctor bills.

5. a. Does Ray write the check?

     b. Does Ray write the checks?

6. a. The chair is black.

     b. The chairs are black.

7. a. I didn't see the tree.

     b. I didn't see the trees.

8. a. The lesson is hard.

     b. The lessons are hard.

Note: In each item, read either *a* or *b*. Do not choose the same letter each time.

PRACTICE 1: Make a List

Write a list of five things you get at the market.

Examples: _a quart of milk_

eggs

1. _____

2. _____

3. _____

4. _____

5. _____

PRACTICE 2: Verb Forms

Use _ever_ and the right form of the verb in the sentence.

Examples: They are the best beans that I _**have ever eaten**_____.
                                                   ever eat

Mrs. King is the best babysitter that Rosa _____.
                                                          ever have

1. This is the best party that we _____.
                                              ever have

2. This is the best cake that I _____.
                                              ever bake

3. Ms. Smith is the best teacher that we _____.
                                                   ever have

4. David is the best friend that Carla _____.
                                                ever have

5. This is the best ham that I _____.
                                              ever eat

PRACTICE 3: Singular and Plural Forms of Nouns

Write the singular or plural form of the missing noun.

Examples: I'll have two _____*glasses*_____ of milk.
                                    glass

I'll have a _____ of coffee.
                        cup

1. Each _____ brings something to eat.
                    person
2. The Masons bring _____.
                            cheese
3. There are eighteen _____ at the party.
                                people
4. For many _____, we have eggs or beans.
                    meal
5. There are three _____ to drink in the ad.
                            thing

PRACTICE 4: Pronouns

Write *my, your, his, her,* or *their.*

Examples: I have a radio. It is _____**my**_____ radio.

The people at the party eat _____ dinner.

1. The Masons are paying _____ bills today.

2. Lee was 16. He had _____ first car.

3. She said, "Did you get hurt when _____ car hit the tree?"

4. She parked _____ car on the street.

5. The women put _____ bags on the table.

6. Lee said, "I was playing cards with _____ friends."

PRACTICE 5: Make Words and Write Sentences

Copy the word. Add -r or -er.
Write the word in a sentence.

Examples: farm ___*farmer*___

___Mr. Arthur is a farmer.___

write _____

_____

1. paint _____

_____

2. bake _____

_____

3. read _____

_____

4. teach _____

_____

5. jump _____

_____

6. sell _____

_____

7. think _____

_____

8. help _____

_____

PRACTICE 6: Story with Missing Words

Write the missing words.

The Class Party

Carla's class is having a dinner party. There will be a big meal.

Each person _____ something to eat. Carla brings

beans. David brings _____ green salad. Jason and Gail

bring baked potatoes. _____ Masons bring apples and

cheese. Other people bring _____ to eat.

Ms. Smith, the teacher, brings the _____. The meat

wasn't cheap. Each person helped to _____ for the meat.

There are eighteen people at _____ party. They are

having fun and eating a _____ meal.

"Please pass the meat," says Ray. "I _____ not eaten

any meat for three days."

Kay _____, "That is right. Meat is not cheap. For

_____ meals, we have eggs, beans, or cheese. They

_____ pretty cheap."

The teacher says, "Please pass the _____. Carla's

beans are the best beans that I have ever eaten."

PRACTICE 1: Verb Forms

Add -d or -ed to the words.

Examples: paint _____painted_____

save _____saved_____

1. clean _____
2. need _____
3. repair _____
4. play _____
5. fix _____

6. work _____
7. bake _____
8. pass _____
9. help _____
10. yell _____

PRACTICE 2: Word Order in Sentences

Put the words in the right order to make a sentence.

Examples: seventeen is Steve

Steve ___is seventeen._____

keys gives Steve some Pete

Pete _____

1. today hard worked you.

   You _____

2. evening six in the from nine works Steve to

   Steve _____

3. will I very take care well of the place

   I _____

4. in Mrs. Green Saturday came on

   On _____

5. is here money the that I today got

   Here _____

PRACTICE 3: Verb Forms

Write *to* and the verb in the sentence.

Examples: Steve's job is _____**to keep**_____ the place clean.

keep

          Pete will teach him _____ radios.

repair

1. He is saving his money _____ a color TV.

get

2. I was going _____ Mrs. Green's radio.

repair

3. Pete is teaching Steve _____ radios and TVs.

fix

4. Each person brings something _____.

eat

5. I need my car _____ to work.

go

6. I went _____ at the wheel.

sleep

7. Jason and Gail planned _____ married.

get

8. We need _____ Ed.

thank

9. It's fun _____ cards.

play

10. He's happy _____ Pete.

help

11. It's hard _____ stairs.

paint

12. It's quicker _____ by car.

go

PRACTICE 4: Questions with *how much* and *how many*

Make a question from the sentence. Use *how much* or *how many*.

Examples: Pete makes $160 a week.

How much *does Pete make?* _____

Jason had two glasses of milk.

How many _____

1. The TV cost $200.

   How much _____

2. Carla has two cups of coffee every day.

   How many _____

3. Steve saved $170.

   How much _____

4. Jason had two ham sandwiches.

   How many _____

5. David had two hamburgers.

   _____

6. The milk cost 75 cents.

   _____

7. Steve works six days a week.

   _____

8. Kay and Ray Mason got seven hundred fifty dollars.

   _____

9. They painted four chairs.

   _____

10. She had some ham.

   _____

PRACTICE 5: Listen

Circle the letter of the sentence that the teacher says.

Examples: a. Pete gives Steve 4 apples.

   b. Pete gives Steve 14 apples.

   a. There are forty people in the class.

   b. There are fourteen people in the class.

1. a. He makes $116 a week.

   b. He makes $160 a week.

2. a. Steve has saved $170.

   b. Steve has saved $70.

3. a. The paint was $4.00 a gallon.

   b. The paint was $14.00 a gallon.

4. a. It's April 16, 2012.

   b. It's April 6, 2012.

5. a. It cost $7.00.

   b. It cost $17.00.

6. a. There are six chairs in the kitchen.

   b. There are sixteen chairs in the kitchen.

7. a. Kim is fifteen.

   b. Kim is fifty.

8. a. His bill was $2.70.

   b. His bill was $2.17.

Note: In each item read either *a* or *b*. Do not choose the same letter each
time. Do not emphasize the endings of the words.

PRACTICE 1: Combine Sentences

Make one sentence from two.

Examples: Carla has an apartment. It is pretty.

Carla has a pretty apartment.

Lee came in. His mother got up.

_____

1. I was 19. I got a job with a hockey team.

_____

2. You go in your cars. You go fast.

_____

3. I like beer. I never drink it.

_____

4. I run the repair shop. It is on Second Street.

_____

5. She yelled. Her face got red.

_____

6. Pete repairs radios. Pete repairs TVs.

_____

7. Steve keeps the shop clean. He keeps the stairs clean.

_____

8. He works in the evening. He works from six to nine.

_____

9. She can read the story. She can read quickly.

_____

10. I was going to repair her radio. I didn't.

_____

PRACTICE 2: Answer Questions

Write short answers to the questions.

Examples: Can you bake a cake? No, <u>I can't.</u>

Will you have a cup of tea? Yes, <u>I will.</u>

1. Were you drinking beer? No, _____

2. Is it half past three? Yes, _____

3. Will you paint the chairs? Yes, _____

4. Can Mrs. Green sleep when her son is late? No, _____

5. Will you have coffee? Yes, _____

6. Is Steve saving his money? Yes, _____

7. Can Steve and Pete fix radios? Yes, _____

8. Has Steve saved $170? Yes, _____

9. Will Lee pay for the tree that he hit? Yes, _____

10. Are you the teenager who hit my tree? Yes, _____

11. Can Steve fix the telephone? No, _____

12. Was Lee going fast when he hit the tree? No, _____

13. Can Pete play on a big hockey team now? No, _____

14. Is Pete a happy person? Yes, _____

PRACTICE 3: Story with Missing Words

Write the missing words.

Pete's Story

Let me tell you my story. I was a teenager in the 1970s. I lived with

_____ mother in Canada. My father _____

dead. When I was nineteen, _____ got a job with a

_____ team in Canada. I was _____

to be a big hockey _____ and make a lot of

_____.

My mother left Canada and _____ back to

Garden City. Then _____ got sick. She needed

_____ to take care of her. _____ came to

Garden City. I _____ a job at a TV _____.

I started repairing TVs. I _____ them in the evening at

_____ kitchen table.

Many years passed. _____ mother did not get well.

_____ never went back to my _____ team.

After fourteen years, I _____ my repair shop.

When I _____ back, I am not very

_____. I was going to be _____ big

hockey player. Many people _____ going to see me play.

_____ was going to make a _____ of

money. These things never _____.

But I am happy with _____ hockey team that

I have _____. There are fifteen teenagers on

_____ team. I am teaching these _____ to

play hockey. They think that I am best hockey player there is.

PRACTICE 4: Listen

Listen to the teacher say the words.
Write the words that have the long sound for e under *eat*.
Write the words that have the short sound for *i* under *it*.

	eat	it
he	*he*	
bill		*bill*
him		
keep		
key		
me		
big		
meat		
sick		
ring		
teach		
team		
miss		
these		
this		

Note: Go over the first two items as examples. Say each word. Point out
that *he* has the long sound for *e* as in *eat*. Point out that *bill* has the
short sound for *i* as in *it*.

44   Lesson 10

PRACTICE 1: *a, an, the*

Write *a, an,* or *the.*

Examples: You need _____*a*_____ license to drive _____*a*_____ car.

You must take _____ written test.

1. To get _____ driver's license, you must take tests. One test

   is _____ eye test. To take _____ eye test, you have to

   read letters on _____ chart. _____ eye test tells if you

   need glasses to drive.

   Another test is _____ written test. If you do not pass

   _____ written test _____ first time, you must not

   drive.

2. Pete runs _____ repair shop on Second Street. Steve works

   for him in _____ evenings. He keeps _____ place

   clean.

   Pete was _____ teenager in _____ 1970s.

   He lived with his mother in Canada. When he was nineteen, he got

   _____ job with _____ hockey team in Canada.

   He was going to be _____ big hockey player and make

   _____ lot of money.

PRACTICE 2: Combine Sentences

Make one sentence from two. Use *if*.

Examples: You want a driver's permit. You must take an eye test.

   If you want a driver's permit, you must take an eye test.

   You do not pass the written test. You must not drive.

   If _____

1. You want to drive a car. You need a driver's license.

   If _____

   _____

2. You want to ride a bicycle. You do not need a driver's license.

   If _____

   _____

3. You can drive well. You can take a driving test.

   If _____

   _____

4. You pass the driving test. You will get a driver's license.

   If _____

   _____

5. You do not pass the driving test the first time. You can take it again.

   If _____

   _____

6. You cannot read the letters on the eye test. You need glasses to drive.

   If _____

   _____

7. You have a permit to drive. You can start driving.

   If _____

   _____

finish (fin ish)

PRACTICE 3: Finish the Sentences

Read the words. Then finish the sentence.

Examples: You need a driver's license if you __want to drive a car.__

You must take tests if you _____

_____

1. You must take an eye test if you _____

_____

2. The eye test tells if you _____

_____

3. You must take a written test. You must not drive if you _____

_____

4. You get a permit to drive if you _____

_____

5. You can start driving if you _____

_____

6. A person with a driver's license must ride with you if you _____

_____

7. You must take a driving test. You will get a driver's license if you _____

_____

8. You can take the driving test again if you _____

_____

PRACTICE 4: Application for a Marriage License

Ellen Miller and Steve Chan are planning to get married. First, they have to get a marriage license. To get the marriage license, they have to fill in an application. Each of them has to fill in part of the application. This is the part that Steve will fill in.

Steve Chan lives at 301 Church Street in Dallas, Texas. His zip code is 75205. His date of birth is May 3, 1978. His place of birth is Dallas, Texas. His mother's name is Molly Chan. Her place of birth is China. His father's name is Robert Chan. His place of birth is China. This is Steve's first marriage.

State of **Texas**

APPLICATION FOR A MARRIAGE LICENSE

Name: _____
            Last Name   First Name

Address: _____
            Number and Street   City   State   Zip Code

Date of Birth: _____   Sex: M F
            Month Day Year

Place of Birth: _____

Father's Name: _____
            Last Name   First Name

Father's Place of Birth: _____

Mother's Name: _____
            Last Name   First Name

Mother's Place of Birth: _____

Is this your first marriage? Yes No   If no, is your wife living? Yes No

PRACTICE 1: Verb Forms

Use the right form of the verb in the sentence.

Examples: Fran _____*was going*_____ to run yesterday, but she didn't.
                                    go

                If you _____ the written test, you get a permit to drive.
                                    pass

1. You _____ a license to drive a car.
                    need

2. When I was 19, I _____ a job with a big hockey team in Canada.
                                get

3. Lee Green _____ to see the tree that he hit.
                        go

4. He _____ at the repair shop for six weeks.
              work

5. I _____ to repair Mrs. Green's radio yesterday, but I didn't.
            go

6. If it is a nice day, Fran _____ in the park.
                                    run

7. I _____ to get a radio, but I didn't have the money.
            go

8. Fran _____ to run in the park yesterday, but she didn't.
                  go

9. While his wife runs, Mike _____ breakfast.
                                      make

10. Fran _____ a mile yesterday.
                  run

PRACTICE 2: Prepositions

Write *in, on, at, of,* or *for.*

Examples: The Whites have a lot _____**of**_____ time.

Every day she gets up _____ five.

1. A lot _____ places give these permits.

2. I get up _____ seven every day.

3. People _____ the park smile _____ Fran.

4. Retired people can get things _____ cheaper prices.

5. Mike lives _____ 1400 Third Street _____ Dallas, Texas.

6. His date _____ birth is April 12, 1940.

7. She will run _____ the mile race.

8. He filled in an application _____ a bus permit.

9. Her breakfast is _____ the table _____ the kitchen.

10. Fran is ready _____ the mile race.

11. He writes one _____ the words _____ each sentence.

12. Did Fran run very far _____ first?

PRACTICE 3: Story with Missing Words

Write the missing words.

Running

Fran White is retired. Fran has been retired for three years.

_____ husband Mike has been retired for five _____.

These days, the Whites have a lot _____ time. The Whites have

time to do _____ that they like.

Fran likes to run. _____ day, she gets up at five and

_____. She is getting ready for a big _____. It is a

mile race for retired _____.

Fran must run five miles every day. _____ she will not get

tired in the _____ race.

Fran has been running every day _____ three years.

Her doctor said that it _____ OK. At first, Fran did not run

_____ far or very fast. Every week, she _____ a little

more.

Sometimes, Fran runs in _____ park. Sometimes, she

runs in the street. _____, Fran is running in the park. It

_____ a nice day. People in the park _____ at Fran.

Fran smiles back at them.

_____ his wife runs, Mike makes breakfast. He

_____ to make breakfast while his wife is _____ in

the kitchen.

When Fran comes back, _____ is ready. Her husband

smiles and says, "_____ it a nice day?"

"Yes," says his _____. "It is a very nice day."

While _____ are eating, Mike looks at his wife.

"_____ you tired, dear?" he asks. "Sometimes, you

_____ very tired."

"Well, I didn't get tired _____," Fran says to her husband.

"And I _____ getting fast. I think I am ready for the mile race."

PRACTICE 4: Listen

Circle the letter of the sentence that the teacher says.

Examples: a. I like them.

b. I like him.

a. I watched them.

b. I watched him.

1. a. Ed is teaching them.

b. Ed is teaching him.

2. a. I'll give them the bicycle.

b. I'll give him the bicycle.

3. a. Carla loves them.

b. Carla loves him.

4. a. The woman paid them.

b. The woman paid him.

5. a. The doctor helped them.

b. The doctor helped him.

Note: In each item, read *a* or *b*. Do not choose the same letter each time.
Do not emphasize the pronouns *them* and *him*.

PRACTICE 5: Application for a Parking Permit

You may need a permit to park at work. To get the permit, you have to fill in an application.

Here is an application for a parking permit. Fill it in for Ms. Jane Fisher. She lives at 30 Baker Street in Dallas, Texas. Her zip code is 75234. She works at the Color Center Paint Factory in Building 3. Her car is a red Ford. The license number of her car is ADU 1010. Do not sign your name. Sign Jane Fisher's name.

Color Center
PAINT FACTORY

APPLICATION FOR A PARKING PERMIT

Last Name: _____ First Name: _____

Address: _____
         Number and Street

_____
         City   State   Zip Code

Building Number: _____

Car License: _____

Color of Car: _____

Make of Car: _____

Sign Here: _____

PRACTICE 1: Finish the Sentences

Use the words at the left to finish the sentence.

Examples: (Fran, run)   It's time **_for Fran to run._**

               (Mike, make breakfast) It's time _____

1. (the Whites, eat)   It's time _____

2. (Steve, get up)   It's time _____

3. (us, go shopping) It's time _____

4. (Pete, retire)   It's time _____

5. (me, go)   It's time _____

PRACTICE 2: Word Order in Sentences

Put the words in the right order to make a sentence.

Examples: got to Mike breakfast make up

               Mike **_got up to make breakfast._**

               you crying why have been

               Why _____

1. Tom died has brother my

   My _____

2. if cry you better you feel will

   You _____

3. 55 was he just

   He _____

4. air Mike line telephoned the

   Mike _____

5. tie where black is your

   Where _____

PRACTICE 3: Make Questions

Make a question from the sentence.

Examples: Fran has been crying.

   <u>**Has Fran been crying?**</u>

   Fran was sitting next to the telephone.

   _____

1. Mike was making breakfast.

   _____

2. Fran has been thinking of her brother.

   _____

3. Jane was drying the dishes.

   _____

4. Fran has been getting ready for the mile race.

   _____

5. Mike has been retired for five years.

   _____

6. Kay has had a driver's license for six years.

   _____

7. Pete has lived in Garden City for many years.

   _____

8. The boys were playing hockey yesterday.

   _____

9. Lee was driving fast when he hit the tree.

   _____

10. Steve has been working for Pete for six weeks.

   _____

PRACTICE 4: Listen

Circle the letter of the sentence that the teacher says.

Examples: a. Why did he have to die?

            b. Why did she have to die?

            a. Mike telephones the air line.

            b. Mike telephoned the air line.

1. a. Think of the happy times you had with them.

   b. Think of the happy times you had with him.

2. a. She asked him a question.

   b. He asked him a question.

3. a. I heard them.

   b. I heard him.

4. a. He got up to make breakfast.

   b. She got up to make breakfast.

5. a. She packed his bag.

   b. He packed his bag.

6. a. You need the black tie.

   b. You needed the black tie.

7. a. It is time for Fran to run.

   b. It was time for Fran to run.

8. a. You have happy times with him.

   b. You had happy times with him.

9. a. They pack their bags.

   b. They packed their bags.

Note: In each item, read *a* or *b*. Do not choose the same letter each time.

PRACTICE 1: Prepositions That Go with Verbs

Write *for, of, back, to,* or *at.*

Examples: I look _____**for**_____ the bright lights again.

I listen _____ music every day.

1. When I go _____ to China, I'll have a better job.

2. I am looking _____ my bicycle. It's not here.

3. I think _____ my family that I left behind.

4. I am listening _____ the radio.

5. While they are eating, Mike looks _____ his wife.

6. Try to think _____ the happy times.

7. People in the park smile _____ Fran.

8. Fran goes running. When she comes _____ home, she eats breakfast.

9. You can take care _____ the shop.

10. I had to go _____ home to get some money.

11. Will you paint my kitchen? I will pay you _____ it.

12. He is taking pictures _____ Gail and Jason.

PRACTICE 2: Make Questions with *why*

Write questions. Use the word *why*.

Examples: Lee Chan feels sad.

Why *does Lee Chan feel sad?*

He is on a night flight to the States.

Why _____

1. Lee Chan is going to the States to study.

   Why _____

2. Lee Chan is sad.

   Why _____

3. Fran cried when her brother died.

   Why _____

4. Fran is tired.

   Why _____

5. You need a driver's license.

   Why _____

6. Pete had to take care of his mother.

   Why _____

7. Pete likes to play hockey.

   Why _____

8. The woman yelled at Lee Green.

   Why _____

9. Lee Chan wants to study in the States.

   Why _____

10. Lee Chan has to take a flight to Dallas, Texas.

   Why _____

PRACTICE 3: Word Order in Sentences

Add the words to the sentence.

Examples: (gray)   They got two quarts of paint.

They _got two quarts of gray paint._

(night)   I am on a flight.

I _____

1. (still)   The lights are in sight.

   _____

2. (again)   I look for the bright lights.

   _____

3. (very)   I will study hard.

   _____

4. (better)   I'll have a job.

   _____

5. (any more)   I will not be sad.

   _____

6. (bright)   I see a light again.

   _____

7. (just)   He was 55.

   _____

8. (there)   We must fly today if we can.

   _____

9. (for 25 years)   Mr. Roberts worked at the Hill Bicycle Shop.

   _____

10. (other)   You can get many things cheaper.

   _____

11. (office)   I telephoned the state building.

   _____

credit (cred it)   single (sing gul)

PRACTICE 4: Application for a Credit Card

This is part of an application for a credit card. Fill it in for Kim Lopez. She lives at 1200 Second Street in Dallas, Texas. Her zip code is 75210. Her telephone number is 447-6800. Her date of birth is May 3, 1991. Her place of work is the Big D Snack Shop. She is single. Her pay is $320 a week. Her bank is the Dallas City Bank.

APPLICATION FOR A CREDIT CARD

Name: _____
           Last Name   First Name

Address: _____
           Number and Street   City   State   Zip Code

Telephone: _____

Date of Birth: _____   Sex: M F   Married   Single
           Month Day Year

Place of Work: _____

Pay Each Week: $ _____

Name of Bank: _____

PRACTICE 5: Story with Missing Words

Write the missing words.

A Night Flight from China

My name is Lee Chan. I am on a night flight. I'm high in the sky.

_____ night is dark. But the _____ lights of my city

are _____ in sight. The bright lights _____ China are

still in sight.

_____ am going far away, and _____ feel sad.

I'm on a _____ flight from China to the _____. I'm

going to the States _____ study.

From high in the _____, I look for the bright

_____ again. But they are not _____ sight. My city is

far _____ me.

I think of my _____ that I left behind. I _____ my

wife and my child _____. I will not see them _____

four years. My child will _____ five by then. A child

_____ a father, but I will _____ be there. Am I doing

_____ right thing?

What will I _____ in the States? Will I _____

a place to live? Will _____ find friends? Am I doing

_____ right thing?

I must not _____ like that. It makes me

_____. I am doing the right _____. I'll be OK in the

_____. I will study very hard. _____ I go back to

China _____ have a better job. I _____ take care of

my family _____. I can help China. I can make things better for

my child and other children.

PRACTICE 1: Pronouns

Write *I, me, my, myself, you, her, he, his,* or *their.*

Examples: Mike smiles at _____his_____ wife.

Fran runs every day. _____ doctor said that it was OK.

1. Jane, I have something sad to tell _____.

2. I am by _____ for the first time.

3. My husband Tom died in _____ sleep.

4. One day, Tom was feeling fine. The next day, _____ was dead.

   I can still see _____ bright smile.

5. Tom's sister and _____ husband arrived that night.

6. My two sons came with _____ wives.

7. I have never lived by _____ in _____ life.

8. Mike asked Fran, "Why have _____ been crying?"

9. Lee Chan misses _____ wife and child.

10. When Fran runs in the park, people smile at _____.

11. I'm running as fast as _____ can.

12. While Fran is running, _____ husband Mike makes breakfast.

13. Fran and Mike finish _____ breakfast.

14. Lee Chan had to get a picture for _____ ID card.

15. After the race, Fran dried _____ face.

PRACTICE 2: Verb Forms

Use the right form of the verb in the sentence.

Examples: Ellen _____*was*_____ sad when her husband died ten days ago.
　　　　　　　　　　be

　　　　　　 Ellen __*has never had*__ a job in her life.
　　　　　　　　　 never, have

1. 　Ellen's husband Tom died ten days ago. Ellen _____
　　　　　　　　　　　　　　　　　　　　　　　　　　　be

   alone now. She _____ sad. She _____
　　　　　　　　　 be　　　　　　　　　　　　　　　miss

   Tom. Ellen _____ by herself in her life. She
　　　　　　　 never, live

   _____ a job in her life. She _____ her life
　　 never, have　　　　　　　　　　　　　　　 must, start

   again.

2. 　Lee came to Dallas, Texas, from China two weeks ago. The first

   week that he was in Dallas, he _____ a lot to do. Lee
　　　　　　　　　　　　　　　　　　 have

   _____ to sign up for classes. He _____ to
　　 have　　　　　　　　　　　　　　　　　　　　 have

   fill in many applications. At last, he _____ ready to start
　　　　　　　　　　　　　　　　　　　　 be

   classes.

   　Lee _____ to class for five weeks now. He
　　　　　 go

   _____ very hard for five weeks. His English
　 study

   _____ much better.
　 get

PRACTICE 3: Write Sentences with *must* and *can*

A. Write five sentences.
   Tell five things that a person must do to get a driver's license.

Examples: You ___must be 16.___

   You ___must fill in an application.___

1. You _____

   _____

2. You _____

   _____

3. You _____

   _____

4. You _____

   _____

5. You _____

   _____

B. Write five sentences. Tell five things that you can do.

Examples: I ___can drive a car.___

   I ___can make breakfast.___

1. I _____

2. I _____

3. I _____

4. I _____

5. I _____

PRACTICE 1: *one, it*

Write *one* or *it.*

Examples: I have a gold sofa. I don't like _____**it**_____.

I filled in an application yesterday. Now, I have to fill in another _____.

1. After Tony Romano's sofa was stolen, he needed another _____.

2. He looked at the green sofa. He wanted _____.

3. Which is cheaper, the gray sofa or the gold _____?

4. Tony's gold ring was stolen. It was his mother's, so he loved _____.

5. Tony's gold ring was his mother's wedding ring. He cannot get another _____
   like _____.

6. The race started at two o'clock. _____ was a mile race.

7. Where is your black tie? You will need _____.

8. I have a black dress, but I want a white _____.

9. Here is an application for a bus permit. Fill _____ in.

10. Which is older, the white kitchen table or the gray _____?

11. Mike makes breakfast. He and Fran eat _____ after she runs.

12. I need an ID card. I will get _____ today.

herself (her self)

PRACTICE 2: Pronouns

Write *myself, yourself, himself,* or *herself.*

Examples: She lives by _____ **herself** _____.

I cut _____.

1. Ann was singing to _____.

2. Did you hurt _____?

3. Help _____ to some cake.

4. Ed was cleaning the kitchen by _____.

5. I like to study by _____.

PRACTICE 3: Write Sentences

Write three sentences. Tell what you like to do by yourself.
Use *by myself* in each sentence.

Examples: _I like to work by myself._ _____

1. _____

2. _____

3. _____

PRACTICE 4: Story with Missing Words

Write the missing words.

The Door Was Open

Tony Romano lives in a big apartment building. One evening after work, Tony got _____ to his apartment very late. The _____ was open, and the lock was _____.

"Oh, no!" Tony said. "Someone has _____ into my apartment. I'll go next _____ and telephone the police."

Tony told _____ police, "My name is Tony Romano. _____ live at 118 Valley Drive, Apartment 10-B. _____ has broken into my apartment. The _____ was open when I arrived from _____. The door was open, and the _____ was broken. I cannot tell if _____ is in there, so I didn't _____ in. I am telephoning from next _____."

"You did the right thing," said _____ police officer. "We'll send a car _____ away."

Two police officers arrived very _____. Both of them had guns. One _____ went into Tony's apartment. The other _____ stayed at the door. They didn't _____ anyone, so both officers went next _____ to get Tony.

"Are you Tony Romano?" _____ officer asked.

"Yes, I am," Tony _____. "Did you find anyone?"

"No one _____ there when I went in," said _____ other officer. "But someone has been _____. Let's go and see what was _____."

"Oh, my sofa!" said Tony. "My _____ was stolen! It was a gold _____, and it wasn't very old." Tony _____ here and there. "Both my TV and my clock radio were stolen," he said.

PRACTICE 5: Listen

Circle the letter of the sentence that the teacher says.

Examples: a. I am a teacher.

b. I'm a teacher.

a. We will give you the money.

b. We'll give you the money.

1. a. We will listen to music on the radio.

   b. We'll listen to music on the radio.

2. a. I am spending a lot of money.

   b. I'm spending a lot of money.

3. a. He is in my class.

   b. He's in my class.

4. a. I will write Fran a letter.

   b. I'll write Fran a letter.

5. a. It is late.

   b. It's late.

Note: In each item, read *a* or *b*. Do not choose the same letter each time.

PRACTICE 1: Pronouns

Write *anything, something, anyone, someone, everyone,* or *no one.*

Examples: Is _____ **anyone** _____ still in the burning building?

No, _____ is in there.

1. In a fire, don't try to save _____.

2. Get _____ away from the burning building fast.

3. I didn't eat _____ today.

4. I want to buy my wife _____ nice.

5. Gail doesn't like _____ to wear her things.

6. I think that _____ is standing behind the door.

7. Uncle Bud gave gifts to _____ in the family.

8. _____ broke into Tony's apartment.

9. The police officer didn't find _____ in Tony's apartment.

10. I need _____ to help me pick up this heavy box.

11. Was _____ in Tony's apartment?

No, _____ was there.

12. Is _____ in the class sixty years old?

No, _____ is sixty.

PRACTICE 2: Prepositions

Write *in, on,* or *at.*

Examples: They put water _____**on**_____ the fire.

           He sometimes smoked _____ bed.

1. Joe went to sleep with his cigarette _____ his hand.

2. The puppy jumped _____ the bed.

3. It was late _____ night.

4. A fire truck arrived _____ Joe's home very quickly.

5. Men and women came _____ the fire truck.

PRACTICE 3: Prepositions That Go with Verbs

Write *up, at, on,* or *of.*

Examples: Joe woke _____**up**_____.

           Joe picked _____ the puppy and ran.

1. "We'll work _____ it," said the police officer.

2. We laughed _____ the stories.

3. Lee Chan had to sign _____ for classes.

4. I will never stop thinking _____ Tom.

5. Joe put _____ his robe.

drove	driven (driv en)	since (sins)
wrote (rote)	given	(giv en)

...ntence.
...m the box.

...asn't _____ **stolen** _____.

...eople _____ little things.

_____ Tony's clock radio while he was at work.

_____ anything in his life.

____ **broken** ____ into my apartment.

_____ two glasses yesterday.

_____ a glass when I do the dishes.

_____.

...e _____ my car every day.

_____ my car to work yesterday.

_____ to church every Sunday.

_____ their car many miles since they go it.

write
wrote
written

13. Mr. and Mrs. Stone _____**write**_____ to their son every week.

14. They _____ him yesterday.

15. Gail _____ a thank you letter to Carla for the wedding gift.

16. Gail has _____ many thank you letters since her wedding.

17. I _____ to my mother every month.

eat
ate
eaten

18. The cake was _____**eaten**_____.

19. Fran and Mike _____ breakfast every morning.

20. Someone _____ the cake last night.

21. Ed and Pete _____ the sandwiches yesterday.

22. Bob has _____ lunch at Fran's Snack Shop every day for two months.

23. I have not _____ anything since this morning.

give
gave
given

24. I didn't buy this ring. It was _____**given**_____ to me.

25. When Joe Stone phoned the fire department, he _____ his name and address.

26. The Stones _____ money to their church every week.

27. I have not _____ a wedding gift to Gail and Jason yet.

PRACTICE 5: Write Sentences

Write sentences. Use the verbs.
Tell what you do or did.

Examples: get up   _I got up at 8 a.m. this morning._

think of   _I am thinking of my family._

1. put on _____

2. sign up _____

3. work on _____

4. get up _____

5. pick up _____

6. live on _____

7. go away _____

8. come back _____

9. take care of _____

10. fill in _____

PRACTICE 1: Prepositions

Write *in, by, on, at, to, from,* or *for.*

Examples: They spent the day fishing _____**on**_____ the lake.

Camping _____ October is fun.

1. There is a state park _____ Green Lake.

2. It's cold _____ the lake _____ October.

3. Mrs. Oak and Joan were _____ the road by seven o'clock.

4. They got _____ Shore Road _____ eight o'clock.

5. _____ the end of the day, they each had six fish.

6. When they got _____ the shore, Mrs. Oak made a fire.

7. Ellen was Tom's wife _____ twenty-nine years.

8. Get everyone away _____ the burning building fast.

9. Keep the numbers of the police and fire department _____ your telephone.

10. Phone the fire department _____ next door or _____ a pay phone.

11. The timetable has flights _____ and _____ many cities.

12. _____ the left are flights that arrive _____ other cities.

13. Flight 240 departs _____ 9:25 a.m.

14. The bright lights of China are still _____ sight.

15. Lee Chan is going _____ Dallas _____ plane.

PRACTICE 2: Combine Sentences

Make one sentence from two.

Examples: Fran did not win the race. She ran in it.

Fran did not win the race that she ran in.

Mrs. Oak was wearing a heavy coat. The coat was her husband's.

Mrs. Oak was wearing her husband's heavy coat.

1. She toasted the bread. She cut the bread from the loaf.

    _____

    _____

2. Mrs. Oak made a fire. They got to shore.

    _____

    _____

3. Someone stole my old gold ring. The ring was my mother's.

    _____

    _____

4. They loaded many things. They needed the things to go camping.

    _____

    _____

5. Fran ran in the race. The race was for retired women.

    _____

    _____

6. They take the road. The road is the best one to Mud Lake.

    _____

    _____

7. Lee had to fill in many applications.
The applications asked for his name, address, and many other things.

_____

_____

8. I am writing a letter to a friend. The friend is very dear to me.

_____

_____

9. Lee is on a night flight. The flight is going from China to the States.

_____

_____

10. The timetable has many flights. The flights arrive from other cities.

_____

_____

11. Lee thinks of his family. He left his family in China.

_____

_____

12. The police opened the door of the apartment. The apartment was broken into.

_____

_____

13. Tony fixed the lock. The lock was broken.

_____

_____

14. I am listening to the radio. Ed gave me the radio.

_____

_____

PRACTICE 3: Story with Missing Words

Write the missing words.

Camping in October

"Let's go camping this weekend," said Joan to her mother. "There is a state park at Green Lake. It's on Shore Road. We can rent a boat there."

"Fine," said Mrs. Oak. "I think _____ camping in October is fun. What _____ we take to eat? Let's see, _____ need coffee, apples, cheese, eggs, and _____ loaf of bread. Shall we take _____ meat?"

"No, we'll go fishing," Joan _____ her mother. "We can roast fish _____ a fire. Wear old clothes, and _____ a heavy coat. It's cold at _____ lake in October, and sometimes it _____."

On Saturday, Joan and her mother _____ the back end of their truck. _____ loaded their tent and two sleeping _____ into the truck. They loaded other _____ that they needed.

Mrs. Oak and _____ were on the road by seven _____. Mrs. Oak was wearing old clothes _____ her husband's heavy hunting coat. Joan _____ wearing old clothes and a heavy _____.

They got to Shore Road at eight _____. The state park was at the _____ of the road. After they put _____ their tent, Mrs. Oak went to _____ a boat. Joan cut the loaf _____ bread and made cheese sandwiches.

The two _____ spent the day fishing on the _____. At the end of the day, they each had six fish.

PRACTICE 4: Listen

Circle the letter of the sentence that the teacher says.

Examples: a. Pete gives Steve a key.

              b. Pete gives Steve the key.

              a. I do not have a timetable.

              b. I do not have the timetable.

1. a. I run a repair shop on Second Street.

   b. I run the repair shop on Second Street.

2. a. Ed has eaten a sandwich.

   b. Ed has eaten the sandwich.

3. a. Tony fixed a lock.

   b. Tony fixed the lock.

4. a. Mrs. Oak went to rent a boat.

   b. Mrs. Oak went to rent the boat.

5. a. Joan cut a loaf of bread.

   b. Joan cut the loaf of bread.

Note: In each item, read either *a* or *b*. Do not choose the same letter each time.
       Do not stress *a* and *the*. Do not pronounce them /ay/ and /thee/.

PRACTICE 1: Add the Ending *-ly* to Words

Write the word. Add *-ly* to make a new word.

Examples: slow   _____ **slowly** _____

   quick   _____

1. sad   _____   7. cost   _____

2. glad   _____   8. quick   _____

3. dear   _____   9. high   _____

4. open   _____   10. week   _____

5. light   _____   11. month   _____

6. cheap   _____   12. year   _____

PRACTICE 2: Use *-ly* Words in Sentences

Write the words with *-ly* in the sentences.

Examples: Ann smiled _____ **sadly** _____.
                                                              sad

   She gets paid _____.
                                               week

1. He goes to the doctor _____.
                                                              year

2. Kay drives her car _____ in the snow.
                                                      slow

3. It is raining so _____ that we can still go fishing.
                                                  light

4. Jason helped his mother _____.
                                                              glad

5. She loves her children _____.
                                                          dear

PRACTICE 3: Verb Forms with *-ing* and *-ed*

Write the missing verb forms in each line.

Examples:	Verb	With *-ing*	With *-ed*
	_____ **stop** _____	stopping	stopped
	hope	_____ **hoping** _____	hoped
	try	trying	_____ **tried** _____
1.	_____	_____	loaded
2.	rain	_____	_____
3.	_____	planning	_____
4.	_____	marrying	_____
5.	smoke	_____	_____
6.	_____	working	_____
7.	follow	_____	_____
8.	_____	missing	_____
9.	cry	_____	_____
10.	_____	cleaning	_____
11.	drop	_____	_____
12.	_____	_____	added
13.	live	_____	_____
14.	_____	asking	_____
15.	_____	_____	baked
16.	dry	_____	_____
17.	_____	_____	hurried
18.	love	_____	_____

PRACTICE 4: Verb Forms in the Past Tense

Write the past tense of the verb.

Examples: get _____*got*_____

run _____

1. say _____
2. cut _____
3. have _____
4. break _____
5. make _____

6. hit _____
7. do _____
8. go _____
9. give _____
10. pay _____

PRACTICE 5: Use Past Tense Verb Forms

Write the past tense of the verb in the sentence.

Examples: I _____*said*_____ OK.
                          say

Rosa _____ the meat and the bread.
            cut

1. Ed _____ his leg last week.
         break
2. Carla _____ a cake yesterday.
            make
3. I _____ my landlady some money last month.
      give
4. The Masons _____ their phone bill yesterday.
                   pay
5. Lee Green _____ a tree with his car last week.
                 hit
6. I _____ the child some stories yesterday.
      tell

PRACTICE 6: Verb Forms with *to*

Use *to* and the verb in the sentence.

Examples: Sam stops _____ **to help** _____ the driver.
                               help

   I don't know what _____.
                              do

1. I was happy _____ you.
                      help

2. It's no fun _____ stuck in the snow.
                     get

3. The man does not know where _____.
                                        go

4. Jason can tell you what _____.
                                  do

5. What is the best road _____ from Apple Valley to Mud Lake?
                                take

6. Mrs. Oak went _____ a boat.
                        rent

7. What shall we take _____?
                             eat

8. Joan and her mother went _____ in their sleeping bags.
                                    sleep

9. Don't stop _____ anything with you.
                     take

10. The Stones worked very hard _____ their home.
                                        buy

PRACTICE 7: Combine Sentences with *so ... that*

Make one sentence from two. Use *so ... that.*

Examples: The wind is blowing so hard. It feels colder.

   <u>**The wind is blowing so hard that it feels colder.**</u>

   It is snowing so hard. Sam cannot see the road.

_____

1. He is going fast. He will miss the turn up ahead.

_____

2. There is so much snow on the road. It is hard to drive.

_____

3. The yellow car throws so much snow onto Sam's car windows. He must clean them.

_____

_____

4. He drinks so much coffee. He can't sleep at night.

_____

5. Ed is so angry. He can't say anything.

_____

6. The sun is so bright. I can't see.

_____

7. This dress is so cheap. Kay wants to buy it.

_____

8. The box is so heavy. I can't pick it up.

_____

9. Fran is so sad. She cries a lot.

_____

*new

PRACTICE 1: Building New Words

Combine each word in List 1 with a word from List 2 to make a new word.
You may use words from List 2 more than one time.

List 1	List 2		New Word
1. any	age	1.	anyone
2. teen	times	2.	teenage
3. four	day	3.	
4. him	line	4.	
5. my	one	5.	
6. nine	person	6.	
7. pay	self	7.	
8. sales	thing	8.	
9. under	teen	9.	
10. some		10.	

Note: Go over the first two items as examples.

PRACTICE 2: Combine Sentences with *more than*

Make one sentence from two. Use *more than*.

Examples: The red shirt cost ten dollars. The gray shirt cost twenty dollars.

 The gray shirt cost more than the red shirt did.

Kay makes $320 a week. Steve makes $150 a week.

 Kay makes more money than Steve does.

1. The book costs three dollars. The paper costs one dollar.

   _____

2. Joe smokes three cigarettes a day. Ed smokes ten cigarettes a day.

   _____

3. Kay has eight plates. Carla has twelve plates.

   _____

4. Kay and Ray spent $100. Gail and Jason spent $200.

   _____

   _____

5. There were ten people at Carla's party. There were six people at Kay's party.

   _____

   _____

6. Ham costs $1.79. Hamburger costs $2.19.

   _____

7. A quart of milk costs 99 cents. A half gallon of milk costs $1.79.

   _____

   _____

8. When Jane got her TV fixed, the labor cost $75.00. The parts cost $32.14.

   _____

   _____

PRACTICE 3: Write Sentences with *better than* and *the best*

A. Finish each sentence. Use the two words at the left.
   Tell which one you like better. Use *better than* in each sentence.

   Examples: (rain, snow)   I like ___rain better than snow._____

   (radio, TV)   I like _____

   (red, green)   1. I like _____

   (meat, cheese)   2. I like _____

   (May, October)   3. I like _____

   (camping, fishing)   4. I like _____

   (tea, coffee)   5. I like _____

B. Finish each sentence. Use the words at the left.
   Use *the best* in each sentence.

   Examples: (salad, I)   This is ___the best salad I have ever eaten._____

   (party, we)   This is _____

   _____

   (beans, I)   1. These are _____

   _____

   (teacher, we)   2. She is _____

   _____

   (cake, Mrs. Hunt) 3. This is _____

   _____

   (friend, I)   4. He is _____

   _____

   (letter, you)   5. That was _____

   _____

PRACTICE 4: Make Questions with *which,* and Answer Them

Write questions with *which*. Answer the questions.

Examples: I like coffee better than tea.

Which __do you like better, coffee or tea?__ ? ___Coffee.___

Mike likes the green car better than the red one.

Which _____? _____

1. Carla likes cheese better than eggs.

   Which _____

   _____? _____

2. Ed likes fishing better than camping.

   Which _____

   _____? _____

3. Ray likes hamburger better than cheese.

   Which _____

   _____? _____

4. I like breakfast better than lunch.

   Which _____

   _____? _____

5. Joan likes trucks better than cars.

   Which _____

   _____? _____

6. Sam likes meat better than fish.

   Which _____

   _____? _____

7. Liz likes the color red better than the color yellow.

   Which _____

   _____ ? _____

8. I like salads better than sandwiches.

   Which _____

   _____ ? _____

9. Bob likes bright colors better than dark ones.

   Which _____

   _____ ? _____

10. I like May better than October.

    Which _____

    _____ ? _____

11. I like department stores better than little shops.

    Which _____

    _____ ? _____

12. I like Fridays better than Mondays.

    Which _____

    _____ ? _____

PRACTICE 5: Story with Missing Words

Write the missing words.

At the Department Store

Steve was hurrying up York Street. He was on his way

_____ Porter's Department Store. Porter's was _____

the corner of York Street _____ Fourth Street.

Steve's friend David _____ at the corner. "What's the

_____?" David asked.

"I have to _____ a sport shirt before the _____

closes," Steve said. "I wore _____ brother's best sport shirt last

_____, and I tore it. I _____ the sleeve on the car

_____."

"One time, I wore my _____ shirt and tore it," David said.

"He's still angry that I _____ his shirt."

"I want to _____ another shirt like my brother's

_____ he gets home," said Steve. "_____ in a hurry.

See you _____."

Steve looked at a sign _____ the first floor. It said

_____ men's clothes were on the fourth _____. Steve

hurried up to the _____ floor. He went to the _____

department. "I want a yellow _____ with short sleeves," he told

_____ salesperson.

"The shirts with short _____ are over there," said the

_____.

Steve picked up a red _____ with short sleeves.

It cost nineteen _____. A green shirt cost twenty five

_____. "That one costs more than _____ red one, but

it's a _____ shirt," said the salesperson. "And _____

yellow one is Porter's best _____ shirt," he added.

Steve was _____, "The best shirt will cost _____

most." And he was right. _____ yellow shirt did cost the

_____. It cost thirty dollars.

"I _____ forty dollars," Steve was thinking.

"_____ green shirt is cheaper than _____ yellow one,

and the red _____ is the cheapest. But I _____ have

to buy the one _____ costs the most. The yellow shirt is like my

brother's."

PRACTICE 6: Read and Answer Questions

The Porter Building	
ROOM	
Babysitter Service	415
The Best Bake Shop	206
Bicycle Shop	101
The Camping Store	207
Home Cleaning Services	315
Jack's Repair Shop	217
Dr. Jane Oliver	301
Tom's Telephone Store	111
Dr. Miller White	211

This is the directory of the Porter Building. There are many stores and offices in the building. Look at the building directory, and answer the questions below.

Examples: On which floor can you buy a telephone? __1_____

In which room can you buy a tent? _____

1. On which floor can you find the Best Bake Shop? _____

2. In which room is Dr. Jane Oliver's office? _____

3. On which floor can you find the Bicycle Shop? _____

4. On which floor can you get a babysitter? _____

5. In which room can you buy a cake? _____

6. On which floor can you buy a bicycle wheel? _____

7. On which floor can you find someone to help you clean your home? _____

8. On which floor can you get someone to fix your TV? _____

9. In which room is Dr. Miller White's office? _____

10. On which floor can you buy a tent? _____

Note: Point out that rooms in the 100s are on the first floor, rooms in the 200s are on the second floor, and so on.

he'll (hēl)

PRACTICE 1: Make Negative Sentences

Make the sentence negative.

Examples: I'll need more money.   *I won't need more money.*

I have to buy a yellow shirt.

_____

1. I'll wear my old coat.

_____

2. She needed a lot of things for her apartment.

_____

3. He'll start another fire in his home.

_____

4. He'll smoke again.

_____

5. He can go camping with us.

_____

6. We'll phone you in the morning.

_____

7. Drive fast.

_____

8. Sam can see the road.

_____

9. I run as fast as she does.

_____

10. You can rent bicycles there.

_____

PRACTICE 2: Word Order in Sentences

Add the word to the sentence.

Examples: (night)   I am on a flight.

I _**am on a night flight.**_ _____

(just)   She is 21.

_____

1. (in October)   One day a police officer phoned Tony.

_____

_____

2. (old)   Did you find my gold ring?

_____

3. (yet)   No, we don't have it.

_____

4. (many)   She wanted Joe to live more years.

_____

5. (for Joe)   It was hard to quit smoking.

_____

6. (ever)   I won't smoke again.

_____

7. (alone)   Can you find your way?

_____

8. (sport)   You can wear my coat if you want to.

_____

_____

9. (very)   A fire truck arrived at Joe's home quickly.

_____

_____

10. (any)   Shall we take meat?

_____

11. (slowly)   Sam knows that he must drive in the snow.

_____

_____

12. (sometimes)   It's cold at the lake in October, and it rains.

_____

_____

13. (two)   They loaded a tent and sleeping bags.

_____

14. (quickly)   Joe left the burning building.

_____

15. (instead)   Kay asked Ray to clean the kitchen, but he watched TV.

_____

_____

16. (instead)   Joe wanted to smoke a cigarette, but he ate a sandwich.

_____

_____

PRACTICE 3: Finish the Sentences

A. Read the words, and then finish the sentence.
   Use *need to, want to, care to,* or 4

Examples: You can drive my car if __*you need to.*_____
                                              need to

              Ed can give Ann a gift if _____
                                              want to

1. You can go to the party if _____
                                              want to

2. Ted can go camping if _____
                                              care to

3. I'll pay for the broken window if _____
                                              have to

4. You can ride my bicycle if _____
                                              need to

5. You can watch TV if _____
                                              care to

6. I'll pay up to $75 for a clock radio if _____
                                              have to

B. Finish the sentence any way that you want to.

Examples: Let him fix the lock if __*he can.*_____

              Mike won't visit the Oak family if __*he doesn't want to.*_____

1. Sign the check if _____

2. Don't fly to Dallas if _____

3. Eat the sandwich if _____

4. Drive Ann to Green Lake if _____

5. Molly will give them a wedding gift if _____

   _____

PRACTICE 1: Word Order in Sentences

Put the words in the right order to make a sentence.

Examples: Steve keys gives some Pete

Pete _gives Steve some keys._

North map America is a this of

This _____

1. camp they in lived a refugee

   They _____

2. helped and Hugo Rosa jobs find they

   They _____

3. Cuba teacher in was a music Hugo

   Hugo _____

4. Hugo a band in job a got so

   So _____

5. very the hard Garcias work to had

   The _____

PRACTICE 2: Write Sentences

Write four sentences. Tell four things that you look forward to doing.

Examples: I look forward to _speaking English faster._

I look forward to _____

1. I look forward to _____

2. I look forward to _____

3. I am looking forward to _____

4. I am looking forward to _____

PRACTICE 3: Verb Tenses

Use the right form of the verb in the sentence.

Examples: I (tell) _____<u>tell</u>_____ my son a story every night.

   I (tell) _____<u>told</u>_____ my son a story last night.

   I (tell) ____<u>have told</u>____ my son a story every night since May.

1. Mrs. Lee (make) _____ dinner for her family every night.

   Mrs. Lee (make) _____ dinner for her family last night.

   Mrs. Lee (make) _____ dinner for her family every night for three months.

2. Jason (eat) _____ eggs for breakfast every morning.

   Jason (eat) _____ eggs for breakfast yesterday.

   Jason (eat) _____ eggs for breakfast since he was a young boy.

3. Carla and David (come) _____ to class on time every night.

   Carla and David (come) _____ to class on time last night.

   Carla and David (come) _____ to class on time every night since class started.

4. Kay (have) _____ lunch with her friend every day.

   Kay (have) _____ lunch with her friend yesterday.

   Kay (have) _____ lunch with her friend every day since they started working as salespersons in a music store.

PRACTICE 4: Verb Forms

Write the verb. Use *to* with the verb, or use the verb with the ending *-ing*.

Examples: They finished _____**loading**_____ the truck.
                           load

                She wanted _____ English.
                               speak

1. She learned _____ the menu.
                    read

2. They wanted _____ in the United States.
                  be

3. Don't forget _____ slowly.
                 drive

4. He quit _____ last year.
            smoke

5. A young man stopped _____ me.
                   help

6. Sam tells the man _____ the car.
                rock

7. Let's go _____ by the lake.
            camp

8. We worked very hard _____ this home.
                buy

9. The two women spent the day _____ on the lake.
                    fish

10. Pete is teaching Steve _____ radios.
                repair

11. Lee got tired of _____ applications.
            fill in

12. I will never stop _____ of Tom.
            think

13. Jill learned _____ right and left turns.
           make

14. Mike tried _____ Fran feel better.
           make

15. I'll start _____ while you telephone the air line.
         pack

PRACTICE 5: Story with Missing Words

Write the missing words.

A Family from Cuba

Hugo and Rosa Garcia came from Cuba with their three sons. The Garcia family came to _____ United States with other Cuban _____.

The Cuban refugees came to _____ United States for a better _____. They looked forward to a _____ future for their children. They _____ to be United States citizens.

_____ refugees came from Cuba on _____ boat. They came to Florida. _____ first, they lived in a _____ camp.

A family in Union Park, Florida, _____ friends with the Garcias. They _____ the Garcias find a place _____ live in Union Park. They _____ Hugo and Rosa find jobs.

_____ was a music teacher in _____. He wanted to teach in _____ United States. But he didn't _____ English very well. So Hugo _____ a job in a band. _____ band played on weekends. In _____ mornings, he cut grass and _____ buildings at a university.

Rosa _____ a job in a snack _____. At first, she didn't know _____ words on the menu. So _____ had to work in the _____.

The Garcias had to work very hard. But they looked forward to a better future.

PRACTICE 1: Use *some* and *any*

Use *some* or *any* in the sentences.

Examples: Gail got _____ **some** _____ plates.

She didn't get _____ **any** _____ cups.

David puts _____ salad on his plate.

He doesn't put _____ cheese on his plate.

1. Gail spent _____ time on the telephone.

    She didn't spend _____ time talking to Jason.

2. The Masons paid _____ bills yesterday.

    They don't have _____ bills to pay now.

3. Carla had _____ ham and potatoes.

    She didn't have _____ beans.

4. Fran had _____ coffee.

    She didn't have _____ tea.

5. Gail's uncle was taking _____ pictures.

    He wasn't writing _____ letters.

6. Maria picked _____ green beans very quickly.

    She didn't pick _____ other crops.

Note: Point out to the student that *any* is often used in negative sentences.

PRACTICE 2: Write Sentences

A. Write sentences.
Tell what the person is or is not planning to do.

Examples: (I, start night classes)

I am planning to start night classes.

(We, not, have a baby)

We are not planning to have a baby.

1. (Gail, not, stay home) _____

_____

2. (Jason, get a second job) _____

_____

3. (Gail, not, quit her job) _____

_____

4. (Gail, go back to work) _____

_____

5. (Gail, share babysitting with Mary) _____

_____

B. Write three sentences. Tell what you plan to do.

Example: _I am planning to go fishing this weekend._

1. _____

_____

2. _____

_____

3. _____

_____

C. Write three sentences telling what you can afford to do.
Write three sentences telling what you cannot afford to do.

Examples: I can afford to have a color TV.

I can't afford to get a car.

1. _____

_____

2. _____

_____

3. _____

_____

4. _____

_____

5. _____

_____

6. _____

_____

Note: If this exercise seems too personal, let the students use another person's
name in the sentences.

PRACTICE 3: Story with Missing Words

Write the missing words.

Is Love Enough?

Carlos was watching Maria. Maria was working hard.

_____ picked the green beans _____ quickly. Her

face was _____ from the sun. But _____ looked

lovely. Her hair _____ black. Her eyes were _____

and dark.

Carlos said, "Maria, _____ look lovely."

Maria looked _____ at Carlos. She liked _____

dark face and bright _____. "He's a handsome man,"

_____ said to herself.

"You're _____, Carlos," said Maria. "But please

_____ away. I have to _____ a lot of beans

_____. I have to make _____ for the family."

Maria _____ one of eleven children _____ the

Gomez family. They _____ in a camp for _____

workers. Many migrants lived _____. The migrants followed

the _____. After they picked the _____, they went

to another _____ and picked another crop. _____

picked many crops in _____ places.

Carlos Lopez was _____ a migrant. He worked

_____ the Smith farm where Maria _____ picking

beans. He did _____ jobs there. He lived _____ the

Smith farm. But _____ had no home or _____ of

his own.

Day _____ day, Carlos watched Maria. _____,

he stopped working and _____ to her side.

Carlos _____ to tell her, "Maria, _____ must

have a life _____ your own. Your sisters _____

brothers are not your _____. You don't have to _____

care of them. You _____ be free."

One day, Carlos _____, "Maria, I love you.

_____ away with me and _____ free. Marry me. We

_____ be very happy."

Maria _____ Carlos, but she didn't _____

him. She looked at _____ sadly and said, "One

_____, then another, was in _____. They left the

family _____ marry. But they are _____ free. They

have many _____. They don't have enough _____.

They don't have enough _____ eat."

Maria went on, "My sisters married for love. But is love enough?"

PRACTICE 4: Answer Questions

Write answers to these questions that people use many times.

Examples: What time is it? <u>It's half past six.</u>_____

            What day is it? _____

1. What's your name? _____

2. Where are you from? _____

3. What kind of person is she? _____

   _____

4. What's the matter? _____

   _____

PRACTICE 1: Building New Words

Add -r or -er to make a noun.

Examples: hunt _____ _hunter_ _____

drive _____ _driver_ _____

1. teach _____
2. lead _____
3. bake _____
4. read _____
5. play _____

6. bank _____
7. march _____
8. protest _____
9. teenage _____
10. babysit _____

PRACTICE 2: Write Sentences

Write three things that Helen Keller was able to do
and three things that she was not able to do.

Examples: _She was able to learn to write._ _____

She was not able to read with her eyes. _____

1. _____
2. _____
3. _____
4. _____
5. _____
6. _____

isn't (iz unt)   hasn't (haz unt)

PRACTICE 3: Write Sentences with *yet*

Write the sentences using *yet*.

Examples: His hair is gray.

His hair isn't gray yet.

Kay has had lunch.

Kay hasn't had lunch yet.

1. It is six o'clock.

_____

2. Mike has made breakfast.

_____

3. Her parents trust me.

_____

4. Gail was planning to have a baby.

_____

5. Jason can afford to go to night classes.

_____

6. I have a job.

_____

7. Carla is ready for work.

_____

8. I want to go home.

_____

9. Ray has spent his last cent.

_____

Note: Point out to the student that *yet* is often used in negative sentences.

PRACTICE 4: Prepositions

Write the prepositions in the sentences.

Examples: Stores did not get any money _____ black people.

The fight _____ civil rights went on.

Dr. Martin Luther King Jr. was a man of peace. But he led one

_____ the biggest fights _____ his time. He led the fight

_____ black people's rights.

Dr. King became a civil rights leader _____ a bus boycott. The

boycott started _____ 1955 _____ Montgomery, Alabama.

Dr. King was the minister _____ a church there.

One day after work, Mrs. Rosa Parks got _____ a bus

_____ Montgomery. She sat _____ the back _____

the bus. _____ that time, _____ some states, blacks had to sit

_____ the back. Some white people got _____ the bus after her.

There was no place _____ them to sit.

The bus driver told Mrs. Parks to give _____ her place. But she was

tired. She did not stand _____. The bus driver got a police officer. The

officer arrested her.

Blacks _____ the city were angry. Black ministers and other leaders

met _____ Dr. King's church. "We're tired _____ sitting

_____ the back _____ the bus," one _____ them

said. The others agreed. They planned a bus boycott.

Black people stopped riding the buses. Buses and stores _____ the

city were nearly empty. This made city leaders angry. Dr. King and other black

ministers were arrested. "Sometimes you have to go _____ jail to fight

_____ justice," Dr. King said.

_____ the end, the blacks won. They won _____ court.

U.S. courts said that blacks had the right to sit any place _____ the bus.

LESSON 1

Practice 1
1. works
2. goes
3. works
4. have
5. listen

Practice 2
1. at
2. at
3. on
4. in
5. on
6. at
7. in
8. on

Practice 3
1. car
2. friends
3. shop
4. boxes
5. music
6. letter
7. dishes
8. sandwiches
9. bills
10. dresses

Practice 4
1. Who has a car?
2. Who works at a music shop?
3. Who is a nurse?
4. Who will go for a snack?
5. Who lives at 917 First Street?
6. Who goes to Fran's Snack Shop?
7. Who works hard?
8. Who goes to class after work?

Practice 5
See page 7 in book 3.

LESSON 2

Practice 1
Answers will vary.

Practice 2
1. A radio is on the table.
2. Rosa is my baby.
3. I have worked at the music shop for six months.
4. It is half past six.
5. April was not a bad month.
6. My baby loves her.

Practice 3
1. David is happy that Carla is his friend.
2. Caria is happy that David helps her with Rosa.
3. Caria is happy that Mrs. King loves Rosa.
4. Caria is happy that David is coming to dinner.
5. I am happy that Rosa is singing.
6. I am happy that I am in this class.
7. David is happy that he can help Carla in class.
8. I am happy that you are my friend.

Practice 4
1. a pat
2. a cup, a jar
3. a jar
4. a box
5. a glass
6. a glass
7. a box

Practice 5
Answers will vary.

LESSON 3

Practice 1
The Masons live in an apartment in the city. They are paying their bills today. Ray is looking at the bills. Kay is writing the checks. The Masons have to pay a lot of bills in May. They have to pay the telephone bill for April. They have to pay the water bill for three months. They have to pay Kay's doctor bill. It was for an office visit.

Practice 2
Answers should match information given in the directions, but the date and signature will vary.

Practice 3
1. am
2. is
3. are
4. is, is
5. was
6. were
7. was
8. is
9. are
10. is

Practice 4
1. live/lived/have lived
2. put/put/have put
3. runs/ran/has run
4. helps/helped/has helped

LESSON 4

Practice 1
1. I started work in April.
2. My baby cannot go to work with me.
3. The Masons have to pay a lot of bills in May.
4. They have to pay Kay's doctor bill.
5. Carla and David can come and play cards with us.
6. And we will not have many bills then.
7. We can go away after the next payday.
8. Let's go away the last three days in May.
9. Kay writes a check for the rent.
10. Write your name on the check.

Practice 2
1. I have not painted chairs.
2. Let's not paint the kitchen red.
3. Jason will not fix the stairs.
4. Let's not paint the stairs first.
5. Gail has not had lunch.
6. You have not painted the table and chairs.
7. They will not paint the kitchen red.
8. Rosa cannot go to work with Carla.
9. Let's not play cards today.
10. We cannot live on two hundred dollars.

Practice 3
1. Will we paint the kitchen?
2. Has Gail had paint in her hair?
3. Can you fix the stairs first?
4. Shall we paint the kitchen red?
5. Will Jason fix the stairs first?
6. Has she painted the chairs?
7. Can Jason and Gail paint the kitchen pink?
8. Will you pay for the paint?
9. Shall we paint the stairs first?

LESSON 5

Practice 1
1. Who baked the wedding cake?
2. Where was the party?
3. When did they have the party?
4. Where was the wedding cake?
5. Where are Gail and Jason?
6. What will Gail's uncle take a picture of?
7. Who is Gail writing a thank you letter to?
8. What did Gail and Jason get?

Practice 2
1. Jane, have a cup of coffee.
2. Jane, listen to music on the radio.
3. Kay, pay the bills.
4. Jason, paint the kitchen first.
5. Kitty, don't put milk in the pan.
6. Tom, don't go away now.
7. Jimmy, don't yell at us.
8. Gail, don't paint the stairs first.

Practice 3
1. Yes, let's listen to music on the radio.
2. No, let's not take the children to the wedding.
3. No, let's not stop at the bank after work today.
4. Yes, let's telephone Jane.
5. Yes, let's have some cake.
6. Yes, let's take Liz to the party with us.
7. No, let's not paint the kitchen gray.
8. Yes, let's get two gallons of paint.

Practice 4
See page 31 in book 3.

LESSON 6

Practice 1
1. the
2. the
3. an, a
4. a
5. the
6. a
7. a, the
8. a
9. an
10. a, the
11. an
12. the

Practice 2
1. for
2. to
3. for
4. to, to
5. for
6. to
7. for
8. to
9. for
10. for
11. for
12. to

Practice 3
1. I have never painted a kitchen.
2. Shall we get some black paint?
3. Let's paint the kitchen first.
4. Their landlady paid them for the pink paint.
5. They got one gallon of gray paint.
6. There were some sandwiches and a quart of milk on the table.
7. Jason and Gail got married in Gail's church.
8. It was on a pretty glass plate.
9. I still have not kissed my little girl.
10. She bakes many wedding cakes.

Practice 4
1. Carla works at a music shop.
2. We can have a snack and listen to music.
3. David has a black car.
4. I'll have a ham sandwich and a glass of milk.
5. I am listening to music on the radio.
6. You can paint the stairs and the kitchen.
7. She paid for the pink paint and the gray paint.

8. The wedding cake was on a pretty glass plate.
9. They had coffee and watched TV.
10. They had ham and potatoes

LESSON 7
Practice 1
1. Yes, it is.
2. No, she didn't.
3. No, I wasn't.
4. Yes, you do.
5. Yes, I did.
6. No, they didn't.
7. No, she wasn't.
8. Yes, she was.
9. Yes, she is.
10. Yes, they were.
11. No, she wasn't.
12. Yes, they do.

Practice 2
1. I cannot sleep when you come in late.
2. I wasn't going fast, and I wasn't drinking beer.
3. My car still runs, but the tree that I hit looks bad.
4. I am in bed, but I'm not sleeping.
5. Come in and have a snack with us.
6. The friends played cards and listened to music on the radio.
7. When David came into the apartment, he kissed Carla.
8. They had coffee and watched TV.
9. When they came back from Snake River, Ray said, "We had fun."
10. They ate some cake, but they did not drink coffee.

Practice 3
See page 39 in book 3.

Practice 4
Answers should match the sentences read by the teacher.

LESSON 8
Practice 1
Answers will vary.

Practice 2
1. This is the best party that we have ever had.
2. This is the best cake that I have ever baked.
3. Ms. Smith is the best teacher that we have ever had.
4. David is the best friend that Carla has ever had.
5. This is the best ham that I have ever eaten.

Practice 3
1. person
2. cheese
3. people
4. meals
5. things

Practice 4
1. their
2. his
3. your
4. her
5. their
6. my

Practice 5
Answers will vary.

Practice 6
See page 44 in book 3.

LESSON 9
Practice 1
1. cleaned
2. needed
3. repaired
4. played
5. fixed
6. worked
7. baked
8. passed
9. helped
10. yelled

Practice 2
1. You worked hard today.
2. Steve works from six to nine in the evening.
3. I will take care of the place very well.
4. On Saturday, Mrs. Green came in.
5. Here is the money that I got today.

Practice 3
1. to get
2. to repair
3. to fix
4. to eat
5. to go
6. to sleep
7. to get
8. to thank
9. to play
10. to help
11. to paint
12. to go

Practice 4
1. How much did the TV cost?
2. How many cups of coffee does Carla have every day?
3. How much (money) did Steve save?
4. How many ham sandwiches did Jason have?
5. How many hamburgers did David have?
6. How much did the milk cost?
7. How many days a week does Steve work?
8. How much (money) did Kay and Ray Mason get?
9. How many chairs did they paint?
10. How much ham did she have?

Practice 5
Answers should match the sentences read by the teacher.

LESSON 10
Practice 1
1. When I was 19, I got a job with a hockey team.
2. You go fast in your cars.
3. I like beer, but I never drink it.
4. I run the repair shop on Second Street.
5. When she yelled, her face got red.
6. Pete repairs radios and TVs.
7. Steve keeps the shop and the stairs clean.
8. He works from six to nine in the evening.
9. She can read the story quickly.
10. I was going to repair her radio, but I didn't.

Practice 2
1. No, I wasn't.
2. Yes, it is.
3. Yes, I will.
4. No, she can't.
5. Yes, I will.
6. Yes, he is.
7. Yes, they can.
8. Yes, he has.
9. Yes, he will.
10. Yes, I am.
11. No, he can't.
12. No, he wasn't.
13. No, he can't.
14. Yes, he is.

Practice 3
See page 57 in book 3.

Practice 4

eat		it	
he	meat	bill	ring
keep	teach	him	miss
key	team	big	this
me	these	sick	

LESSON 11
Practice 1
1. To get a driver's license, you must take tests. One test is an eye test. To take the eye test, you have to read letters on a chart. The eye test tells if you need glasses to drive.
   Another test is a written test. If you do not pass the written test the first time, you must not drive.
2. Pete runs a repair shop on Second Street. Steve works for him in the evenings. He keeps the place clean.
   Pete was a teenager in the 1970s. He lived with his mother in Canada. When he was nineteen, he got a job with a hockey team in Canada. He was going to be a big hockey player and make a lot of money.

Practice 2
1. If you want to drive a car, you need a driver's license.
2. If you want to ride a bicycle, you do not need a driver's license.
3. If you can drive well, you can take a driving test.
4. If you pass the driving test, you will get a driver's license.
5. If you do not pass the driving test the first time, you can take it again.
6. If you cannot read the letters on the eye test, you need glasses to drive.
7. If you have a permit to drive, you can start driving.

Practice 3
1. You must take an eye test if you want a driver's license.
2. The eye test tells if you need glasses to drive.
3. You must take a written test. You must not drive if you do not pass the written test.
4. You get a permit to drive if you pass the written test.
5. You can start driving if you have a permit.
6. A person with a driver's license must ride with you if you have a permit.
7. You will get a driver's license if you pass the driving test.
8. You can take the driving test again if you do not pass it the first time.

Practice 4
Answers should match information given in the directions.

LESSON 12
Practice 1
1. need
2. got
3. went
4. has worked
5. was going
6. will run
7. was going
8. was going
9. makes
10. ran

Practice 2
1. of
2. at
3. in, at
4. for
5. at, in
6. of
7. in
8. for
9. on, in
10. for
11. of, in
12. at

Practice 3

See pages 65 and 66 in book 3.

Practice 4

Answers should match the sentences read by the teacher.

Practice 5

Answers should match information given in the directions.

LESSON 13

Practice 1

1. It's time for the Whites to eat.
2. It's time for Steve to get up.
3. It's time for us to go shopping.
4. It's time for Pete to retire.
5. It's time for me to go.

Practice 2

1. My brother Tom has died.
2. You will feel better if you cry.
3. He was just 55.
4. Mike telephoned the air line.
5. Where is your black tie?

Practice 3

1. Was Mike making breakfast?
2. Has Fran been thinking of her brother?
3. Was Jane drying the dishes?
4. Has Fran been getting ready for the mile race?
5. Has Mike been retired for five years?
6. Has Kay had a driver's license for six years?
7. Has Pete lived in Garden City for many years?
8. Were the boys playing hockey yesterday?
9. Was Lee driving fast when he hit the tree?
10. Has Steve been working for Pete for six weeks?

Practice 4

Answers should match the sentences read by the teacher.

LESSON 14

Practice 1

1. back	5. at	9. of
2. for	6. of	10. back
3. of	7. at	11. for
4. to	8. back	12. of

Practice 2

1. Why is Lee Chan going to the States?
2. Why is Lee Chan sad?
3. Why did Fran cry when her brother died?
4. Why is Fran tired?
5. Why do you need a driver's license?
6. Why did Pete have to take care of his mother?
7. Why does Pete like to play hockey?
8. Why did the woman yell at Lee Green?
9. Why does Lee Chan want to study in the States?
10. Why does Lee Chan have to take a flight to Dallas, Texas?

Practice 3

1. The lights are still in sight.
2. I look for the bright lights again.
3. I will study very hard.
4. I'll have a better job.
5. I will not be sad any more.
6. I see a bright light again.
7. He was just 55.
8. We must fly there today if we can.
9. Mr. Roberts worked at the Hill Bicycle Shop for 25 years.
10. You can get many other things cheaper.
11. I telephoned the state office building.

Practice 4

Answers should match information given in the directions.

Practice 5

See page 77 in book 3.

LESSON 15

Practice 1

1. you	9. his
2. myself	10. her
3. his	11. I
4. he, his	12. her
5. her	13. their
6. their	14. his
7. myself, my	15. her
8. you	

Practice 2

1. Ellen's husband Tom died ten days ago. Ellen <u>is</u> alone now. She <u>is</u> sad. She <u>misses</u> Tom. Ellen <u>has never lived</u> by herself in her life. She <u>has never had</u> a job in her life. She <u>must start</u> her life again.
2. Lee came to Dallas, Texas, from China two weeks ago. The first week that he was in Dallas, he <u>had</u> a lot to do. Lee had to sign up for classes. He <u>had</u> to fill in many applications. At last, he <u>was</u> ready to start classes.

   Lee <u>has been going</u> to class for five weeks now. He <u>has been studying</u> very hard for five weeks. His English <u>is getting</u> much better.

Practice 3

Answers will vary.

LESSON 16

Practice 1

1. one	5. one, it	9. it
2. it	6. It	10. one
3. one	7. it	11. it
4. it	8. one	12. one

Practice 2

1. herself	3. yourself	5. myself
2. yourself	4. himself	

Practice 3

Answers will vary.

Practice 4

See page 89 in book 3.

Practice 5

Answers should match the sentences read by the teacher.

LESSON 17

Practice 1

1. anything	7. everyone
2. everyone	8. Someone
3. anything	9. anyone
4. something	10. someone
5. anyone	11. anyone, no one
6. someone	12. anyone, no one

Practice 2

1. in	3. at	5. on
2. on	4. at	

Practice 3

1. on	3. up	5. on
2. at	4. of	

Practice 4

1. stolen	10. drove	19. eat
2. steal	11. drive	20. ate
3. stole	12. driven	21. ate
4. stolen	13. write	22. eaten
5. broken	14. wrote	23. eaten
6. broke	15. wrote	24. given
7. break	16. written	25. gave
8. broken	17. write	26. give
9. drive	18. eaten	27. given

Practice 5

Answers will vary.

LESSON 18

Practice 1

1. at	6. to	11. to, from
2. at, in	7. for	12. On, from
3. on	8. from	13. at
4. to, at (by)	9. by	14. in
5. At (By)	10. from, from	15. to, by

Practice 2

1. She toasted the bread that she cut from the loaf.
2. Mrs. Oak made a fire when they got to shore.
3. Someone stole my mother's old gold ring.
4. They loaded many things that they needed to go camping.
5. Fran ran in the race for retired women.
6. They take the best road to Mud Lake.
7. Lee had to fill in many applications that asked for his name, address, and many other things.
8. I am writing a letter to a very dear friend.
9. Lee is on a night flight (that is going) from China to the States.
10. The timetable has many flights (that arrive) from other cities.
11. Lee thinks of his family (that he left) in China.
12. The police opened the door of the apartment that was broken into.
13. Tony fixed the broken lock.
14. I am listening to the radio that Ed gave me.

Practice 3

See page 101 in book 3.

Practice 4

Answers should match the sentences read by the teacher.

LESSON 19

Practice 1
1. sadly
2. gladly
3. dearly
4. openly
5. lightly
6. cheaply
7. costly
8. quickly
9. highly
10. weekly
11. monthly
12. yearly

Practice 2
1. yearly
2. slowly
3. lightly
4. gladly
5. dearly

Practice 3
1. load	loading	loaded
2. rain	raining	rained
3. plan	planning	planned
4. marry	marrying	married
5. smoke	smoking	smoked
6. work	working	worked
7. follow	following	followed
8. miss	missing	missed
9. cry	crying	cried
10. clean	cleaning	cleaned
11. drop	dropping	dropped
12. add	adding	added
13. live	living	lived
14. ask	asking	asked
15. bake	baking	baked
16. dry	drying	dried
17. hurry	hurrying	hurried
18. love	loving	loved

Practice 4
1. said
2. cut
3. had
4. broke
5. made
6. hit
7. did
8. went
9. gave
10. paid

Practice 5
1. broke
2. made
3. gave
4. paid
5. hit
6. told

Practice 6
1. to help
2. to get
3. to go
4. to do
5. to take
6. to rent
7. to eat
8. to sleep
9. to take
10. to buy

Practice 7
1. He is going so fast that he will miss the turn up ahead.
2. There is so much snow on the road that it is hard to drive.
3. The yellow car throws so much snow onto Sam's car windows that he must clean them.
4. He drinks so much coffee that he can't sleep at night.
5. Ed is so angry that he can't say anything.
6. The sun is so bright that I can't see.
7. This dress is so cheap that Kay wants to buy it.
8. The box is so heavy that I can't pick it up.
9. Fran is so sad that she cries a lot.

LESSON 20

Practice 1
1. anyone
2. teenage
3. fourteen
4. himself
5. myself
6. nineteen
7. payday
8. salesperson
9. underline
10. sometimes (someone, something)

Practice 2
1. The book costs more than the paper does.
2. Ed smokes more (cigarettes) than Joe does.
3. Carla has more plates than Kay does.
4. Gail and Jason spent more (money) than Kay and Ray did.
5. There were more people at Carla's party than at Kay's party.
6. Hamburger costs more than ham does.
7. A half gallon of milk costs more than a quart of milk does.
8. When Jane got her TV fixed, the labor cost more than the parts did.

Practice 3
Answers will vary.

Practice 4
1. Which does Carla like better, cheese or eggs? Cheese.
2. Which does Ed like better, fishing or camping? Fishing.
3. Which does Ray like better, hamburger or cheese? Hamburger.
4. Which do you like better, breakfast or lunch? Breakfast.
5. Which does Joan like better, trucks or cars? Trucks.
6. Which does Sam like better, meat or fish? Meat.
7. Which (color) does Liz like better, red or yellow? Red.
8. Which do you like better, salads or sandwiches? Salads.
9. Which does Bob like better, bright colors or dark ones? Bright ones.
10. Which do you like better, May or October? May.
11. Which do you like better, department stores or little shops? Department stores.
12. Which do you like better, Fridays or Mondays? Fridays.

Practice 5
See pages 113 and 114 in book 3.

Practice 6
1. 2
2. 301
3. 1
4. 4
5. 206
6. 1
7. 3
8. 2
9. 211
10. 2

LESSON 21

Practice 1
1. I won't wear my old coat.
2. She didn't need a lot of things for her apartment.
3. He won't start another fire in his home.
4. He won't smoke again.
5. He can't go camping with us.
6. We won't phone you in the morning.
7. Don't drive fast.
8. Sam can't see the road.
9. I don't run as fast as she does.
10. You can't rent bicycles there.

Practice 2
1. One day in October, a police officer phoned Tony.
2. Did you find my old gold ring?
3. No, we don't have it yet.
4. She wanted Joe to live many more years.
5. It was hard for Joe to quit smoking.
6. I won't ever smoke again.
7. Can you find your way alone?
8. You can wear my sport coat if you want to.
9. A fire truck arrived at Joe's home very quickly.
10. Shall we take any meat?
11. Sam knows that he must drive slowly in the snow.
12. It's cold at the lake in October, and sometimes it rains.
13. They loaded a tent and two sleeping bags.
14. Joe left the burning building quickly.
15. Kay asked Ray to clean the kitchen, but he watched TV instead.
16. Joe wanted to smoke a cigarette, but he ate a sandwich instead.

Practice 3-A
1. You can go to the party if you want to.
2. Ted can go camping if he cares to.
3. I'll pay for the broken window if I have to.
4. You can ride my bicycle if you need to.
5. You can watch TV if you care to.
6. I'll pay up to $75 for a clock radio if I have to.

Practice 3-B
Answers will vary.

LESSON 22

Practice 1
1. They lived in a refugee camp.
2. They helped Hugo and Rosa find jobs.
3. Hugo was a music teacher in Cuba.
4. So Hugo got a job in a band.
5. The Garcias had to work very hard.

Practice 2
Answers will vary.

Practice 3
1. makes		3. come
made		came
has made		have come
2. eats		4. has
ate		had
has eaten		has had

Practice 4
1. to read
2. to be
3. to drive
4. smoking
5. to help
6. to rock
7. camping
8. to buy
9. fishing
10. to repair
11. filling in
12. thinking
13. to make
14. to make
15. to pack

Practice 5
See pages 123–124 in book 3.

LESSON 23

Practice 1

1.–6. some, any

Practice 2-A

1. Gail is not planning to stay home.
2. Jason is planning to get a second job.
3. Gail is not planning to quit her job.
4. Gail is planning to go back to work.
5. Gail is planning to share babysitting with Mary.

Practices 2-B and 2-C

Answers will vary.

Practice 3

See story 2 in *Changes*.

Practice 4

Answers will vary.

LESSON 24

Practice 1

1. teacher	5. player	8. protester
2. leader	6. banker	9. teenager
3. baker	7. marcher	10. babysitter
4. reader		

Practice 2

Answers will vary.

Practice 3

1. It isn't six o'clock yet.
2. Mike hasn't made breakfast yet.
3. Her parents don't trust me yet.
4. Gail wasn't planning to have a baby yet.
5. Jason can't afford to go to night classes yet.
6. I don't have a job yet.
7. Carla isn't ready for work yet.
8. I don't want to go home yet.
9. Ray hasn't spent his last cent yet.

Practice 4

Dr. Martin Luther King Jr. was a man of peace. But he led one <u>of</u> the biggest fights <u>of</u> his time. He led the fight <u>for</u> black people's rights.

Dr. King became a civil rights leader <u>in</u> a bus boycott. The boycott started <u>in</u> 1955 <u>in</u> Montgomery, Alabama. Dr. King was the minister <u>of</u> a church there.

One day after work, Mrs. Rosa Parks got <u>on</u> a bus <u>in</u> Montgomery. She sat <u>at</u> (<u>in</u>) the back <u>of</u> the bus. <u>At</u> that time, <u>in</u> some states, blacks had to sit <u>at</u> (<u>in</u>) the back. Some white people got <u>on</u> the bus after her. There was no place <u>for</u> them to sit.

The bus driver told Mrs. Parks to give <u>up</u> her place. But she was tired. She did not stand <u>up</u>. The bus driver got a police officer. The officer arrested her.

Blacks <u>in</u> the city were angry. Black ministers and other leaders met <u>in</u> (<u>at</u>) Dr. King's church. "We're tired <u>of</u> sitting <u>in</u> the back <u>of</u> the bus," one <u>of</u> them said. The others agreed. They planned a bus boycott.

Black people stopped riding the buses. Buses and stores <u>in</u> the city were nearly empty. This made city leaders angry. Dr. King and other black ministers were arrested. "Sometimes you have to go <u>to</u> jail to fight <u>for</u> justice," Dr. King said.

<u>In</u> the end, the blacks won. They won <u>in</u> court. U.S. courts said that blacks had the right to sit any place <u>on</u> the bus.

WITHDRAWN

Word List

Word	Page	Lesson/Practice
break	71	17-4
broke	71	17-4
can't	42	10-2
China	48	11-4
combine	13	2-3
credit	60	14-4
don't	22	5-2
driven	71	17-4
drove	71	17-4
every	17	3-4
example	7	1-1
finish	47	11-3
Ford	53	12-5
form	8	1-3
given	71	17-4
goes	7	1-1
hasn't	106	24-3
he'll	92	21-1
herself	66	16-2
* how	39	9-4
isn't	106	24-3
* long	44	10-4
make	9	1-4

Word	Page	Lesson/Practice
marriage	48	11-4
negative	19	4-2
* new	84	20-1
* noun	8	1-3
* now	16	3-3
order	12	2-2
* plural	8	1-3
practice	7	1-1
preposition	7	1-2
* pronoun	34	8-4
question	9	1-4
right	12	2-2
* room	91	20-6
since	71	17-4
single	60	14-4
* singular	8	1-3
steal	71	17-4
stole	71	17-4
tense	16	3-3
use	9	1-4
verb	7	1-1
wrote	71	17-4

*Indicates a sight word